2010 *Mathematics Subject Classification*. Primary 00A06, 00A08, 00A09, 00A66, 97A20, 97A80, 97M10, 97M50, 97M80.

For additional information and updates on this book, visit
www.ams.org/bookpages/mbk-104

Library of Congress Cataloging-in-Publication Data
Names: Morgan, David (David Christian)
Title: Y Origami?: Explorations in Folding / David C. Morgan [and four others].
Other titles: Why Origami?
Description: Providence, Rhode Island: American Mathematical Society, [2017] | Includes bibliographical references.
Identifiers: LCCN 2017002522 | ISBN 9781470436742 (alk. paper)
Subjects: LCSH: Origami. | Origami—Mathematics. | AMS: General – General and miscellaneous specific topics – Mathematics for nonmathematicians (engineering, social sciences, etc.). msc | General – General and miscellaneous specific topics – Recreational mathematics. msc | General – General and miscellaneous specific topics – Popularization of mathematics. msc | General – General and miscellaneous specific topics – Mathematics and visual arts, visualization. msc | Mathematics education – General, mathematics and education – Recreational mathematics, games. msc | Mathematics education – General, mathematics and education – Popularization of mathematics. msc | Mathematics education – Mathematical modeling, applications of mathematics – Modeling and interdisciplinarity. msc | Mathematics education – Mathematical modeling, applications of mathematics – Physics, astronomy, technology, engineering. msc | Mathematics education – Mathematical modeling, applications of mathematics – Arts, music, language, architecture. msc
Classification: LCC TT872.5 .Y325 2017 | DDC 736/.982--dc23
LC record available at https://lccn.loc.gov/2017002522

Explorations in Folding

Y ORIGAMI?

David C. Morgan
Denise M. Halverson
Spencer P. Magleby
Terri C. Bateman
Larry L. Howell

AMS
AMERICAN MATHEMATICAL SOCIETY

CONTENTS

FOREWORD

For hundreds of years, the art of folding paper—origami, to use its Japanese name—served two purposes, both aesthetic: entertaining craft and symbolic decoration. In the middle of the twentieth century, though, the practice underwent an artistic renaissance as artists and craftspeople developed new and innovative methods of designing and folding their intended forms. But it also underwent another change: origami came into the world of science and engineering, and both fields have been immeasurably enriched by the meeting.

At first blush, this would seem to be an odd pairing: an ancient Japanese art and the modern, science-driven world of engineering. What could these two practices possibly have in common? What engineering and paper folding share is that both are bound by laws that specify what you can and cannot accomplish, and those laws are effectively described by the language of mathematics. Mathematics is a purely abstract logical system, and yet it has remarkable power in the physical world: it tells cosmologists how the stars and planets dance and tells engineers whether a beam has the strength to support its load. It can also tell an origami artist how much paper to allocate for each feature of the subject, and even the arrangement and number of folds. When mathematical methods came to origami, the art form changed in ways that were unprecedented, resulting in artworks undreamed of by the artisans of old.

An origami artist is usually motivated by aesthetic goals; an engineer by functional requirements. But sometimes—even often—both sets of goals may be satisfied by the physical phenomenon of folding. And when that happens, the tools of artistic origami and the underlying mathematics of the same can be pressed into service to address the needs of the engineer. The folds of origami can create a wide variety of shapes and, as well, a wide range of mechanisms. The mechanical repertoire of origami includes levers, pivots, hinges, force multipliers, distance reducers, conversion of direction of motion, and more. When we combine that versatility with the simplicity and ubiquity of a planar sheet starting material, the match between origami and engineering begins to seem almost natural.

And, amazingly, the same logical system underlies both art and technology. The mathematics that describes origami is agnostic about the application to which it is put. Whether one is creating a bird, insect, or flower, or a solar array, backpack, or furniture, the same principles are at work; the same patterns apply; the same equations describe. We can apply folding to both artistic and technological ends. Because of this duality we find the practitioners of origami moving readily between artistic and technological fields, applying their skills to both, separately and together.

Scientists and engineers often emphasize the formality and rigor of their craft, and with good reason; it is by following the rigor and logic of mathematics and the cumulative growth of knowledge that comes from following the scientific process and the engineering discipline that has led to advances in the human condition. But the dirty little secret of all of the hard scientific fields is that even the most rigorous science, the most formal mathematics, is partly an art. Qualities like elegance and beauty are part and parcel of the scientific endeavor. The wonder of origami is that any given form might find its home in either camp. Is it art? Is it science? Does it matter? Whether used for aesthetics, functionality, or a combination of the two, origami has much to give—and in this book, you will see many examples of both, sometimes emphasizing one, sometimes the other, and sometimes in equal measure.

Robert J. Lang

INTRODUCTION

This book grew out of an exhibit at the Brigham Young University Museum of Art in 2015 that featured origami art from around the world and demonstrated the connections between art, engineering, design, science, and mathematics. The exhibit, "Folding Paper: The Infinite Possibilities of Origami," was also supplemented with designs developed at BYU, where we have conducted research based on the hypothesis that products and engineering systems could be designed to achieve the motions found in origami, with similar levels of efficiency, but using different materials and processes that would enable them to meet emerging product needs. Because origami models start from a flat sheet, they can be made using inexpensive high-production methods; they can be very compact; and they can be made of one piece of material. The results of our research, which were graciously funded by the National Science Foundation, the Air Force Office of Scientific Research, and NASA, among others, have been published in academic journals and conference proceedings because they are mostly theoretical. However, as evidenced by the many examples in this book, our research in origami design and in the mathematical and engineering possibilities latent in the simple act of folding has the potential for immediate and wide-reaching impact.

Who would have thought that the beautiful and ancient art of origami would be a catalyst for new discoveries in science, engineering, design, and mathematics? But origami represents the ultimate efficiency in creating sophisticated motions. Constructed from a single, regular-shaped sheet of paper, it uses only one fabrication process: folding. For centuries artists have invested immeasurable effort developing origami models within these constraints. Because paper is an accessible and formable medium, prototyping vast numbers of possible designs is relatively efficient and effective, resulting in stunning motions in a simple medium that were not previously conceivable using other methods.

To learn to fold may be considered a kindergarten rite of passage, but folding is also a powerful and versatile practice used to build our world. Do you remember when you were first learning to fold? Trying to match up the corners of the paper and make a straight crease, or trying to fold a sheet into a neat square? The rudimentary skills you mastered to correctly fold probably went uncelebrated. However, even as your folding proficiency increased, these fundamental skills also served as the basis for other physical and cognitive abilities you developed. Today, while it has possibly been ages since you refolded a paper map, you understand something about exactness, or how materials behave, or even about operation sequencing because of folding.

This book demonstrates the potential of folding to improve the way things function, to simplify how products are made, and to create new objects that would otherwise be impossible to create. We have organized the example section to display the product prototype next to the work of origami that inspired it. The solar collector, the felt stool, and the surgery tool were all influenced in some way by folding paper. We've tried to include models made from a range of materials and in a range of sizes. This includes everything from a microscopic machine to huge solar panels designed to unfold in outer space. Most of the models are in the prototype phase—meaning that physical hardware has been built to demonstrate the concept, but the models are not necessarily available commercially. This book includes most of the technologies and products featured in the exhibit "Folding Paper: The Infinite Possibilities of Origami," and it also expands into other areas that have not been publicly displayed.

The book's title, *Y Origami?*, was chosen for its double meaning. It addresses the question of "why origami?" or "are there practical uses of origami?", and it also illustrates an answer to that question by showing research that has been done at Brigham Young University, or "The Y."

David C. Morgan
Denise M. Halverson
Spencer P. Magleby
Terri C. Bateman
Larry L. Howell

ORIGAMI-BASED DESIGN

Deployable Solar Array

Materials: Garolite, Kapton film
Diameter: small 10cmx40cm
medium 20cmx144cm
large 2.8cmx25m

INSPIRATION: The deployable solar array was inspired by the origami flasher pattern, developed independently by Shafer and Plamer [1-3]. In its closed state the paper folds up and wraps around the central polygon, but when two opposite edges are pulled it flashes open to its flat state. When the design is modified to allow for thick, nonpaper materials, a wide range of rigid-paneled deployable arrays are possible.

A. Robert Lang modified the flasher pattern to accommodate thickness. The fold lines are piecewise linear. The model is scalable and has been designed for both a large 25-meter array and a small 40-centimeter (CubeSat) array.

B. Modified fold pattern from the original flasher pattern by Jeremy Shafer [2]. "Don't worry, there's nothing unseemly about this Flasher. It's merely an entertaining 'hyper-action' geometric model that expands and contracts. Chris Palmer and I designed it together, using as a base Kawasaki's iso-area twist folding" [Origami to Astonish and Amuse, pg. 110].

A

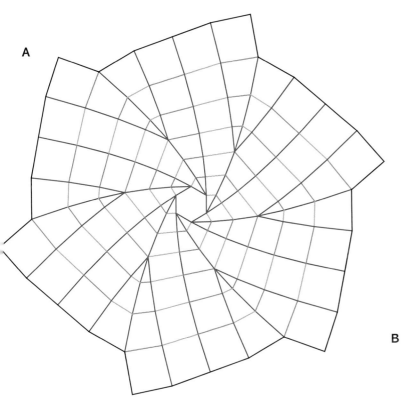

B

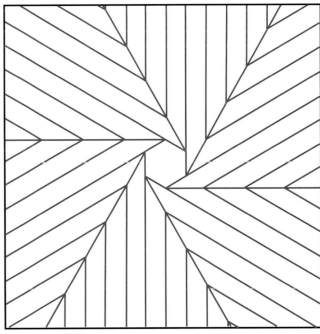

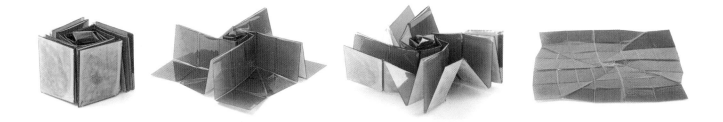

APPLICATION: Very small satellites called CubeSats have specific form factor of $10\times10\times10cm^3$ (1U) which can be joined in series up to 3U. The CubeSat four-sided model of the diameter. It is designed to have two "rings."

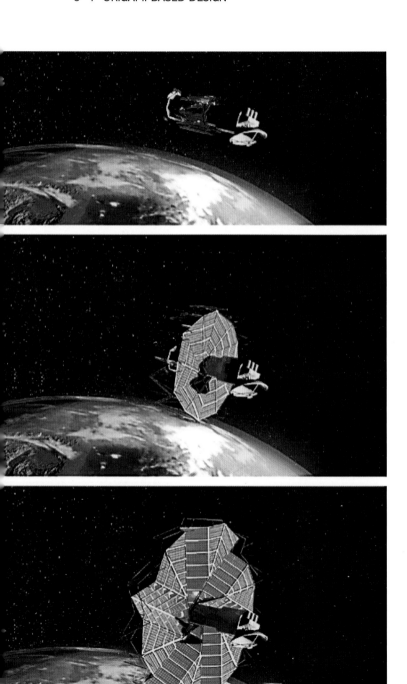

 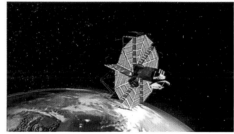 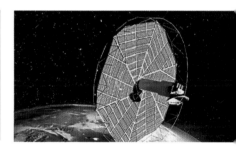

Participants: Shannon
Zirbel, Spencer Magleby,
Larry Howell (BYU); Rob-
ert Lang (Lang Origami),
with NASA Jet Propulsion
Laboratory

APPLICATION: The picture above demonstrates the sequence of a 25-meter
solar array deployment in space. Like the
CubeSat, it also has two rings. We see a
second ring of sectors starting three
elements out from the center, where a
new triangle begins. When deploying, the
outermost ring unfolds fully before the
next ring begins to deploy. The model is
designed to be rigid foldable by including gaps in the membrane between rigid
panels where all of the flexing is concen-
trated. We can also change the number
of sectors (or central polygon shape),
number of rings, and number of elements
in a ring to meet various needs.

Ballistic Barrier

INSPIRATION: The barrier pattern was developed through several small- and large-scale models to meet the requirements of being compact, portable, and protective. The relevant origami pattern of identical degree-4 vertices was first described by David Huffman. In this case the angles and edge lengths were chosen specifically for the requirements of the barrier. This pattern can also be found in an old magician's routine called "Trouble-wit."

The panels are composed of 12 layers of Kevlar® with an inner aluminum composite core, covered in a ballistic nylon outer cover. The creases are achieved through membrane folds in the Kevlar® layers. Testing demonstrated a prototype version of the barrier was able to stop several close-range bullet rounds and remain stable and intact.

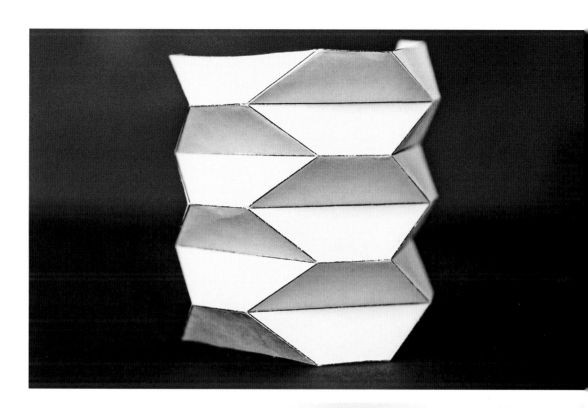

Participants: Many
students and faculty
from BYU CMR Lab

APPLICATION: This folded barrier is portable, deploy-able, and bulletproof. It was created to be compact in its stowed state and deployed into a stable structure to provide front and flank ballistic protection. The barrier could be used by police, SWAT, military, or in schools and other public places.

Oriceps

Materials: polypropylene,
polycarbonate,
amorphous metals
Size: handheld to micro
scale

INSPIRATION: The oriceps were inspired by Jeremy Shafer's chomper [3], an origami fold that looks like a chomping mouth. When the teeth are removed, this fold pattern becomes a simple gripper that "bites" up and down when the back is squeezed in and out. To create the oriceps, the chomper fold pattern was modified to create a flat rather than a creased gripping surface; fold angles were adjusted to achieve more desirable motion; and material was cut out along the folds to enable the use of thick, non-paper materials.

APPLICATION: Intended for use as forceps in minimally invasive surgical applications, the oriceps have the benefits of being made of a single piece of material, scalable to different sizes, and producible using 2-D fabrication methods, such as stamping or laser cutting. Oriceps could be used as disposable surgical tools in cases where using cleaning tools is difficult or expensive. Oriceps could also be used in nonsurgical applications where they must be small for insertion and then open up into the functional gripping form, such as disaster response and recovery or space exploration.

Jeremy Shafer's chomper

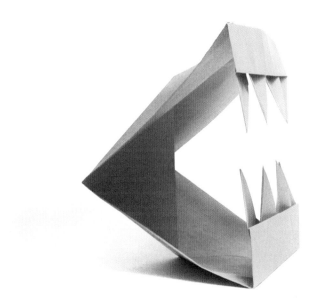

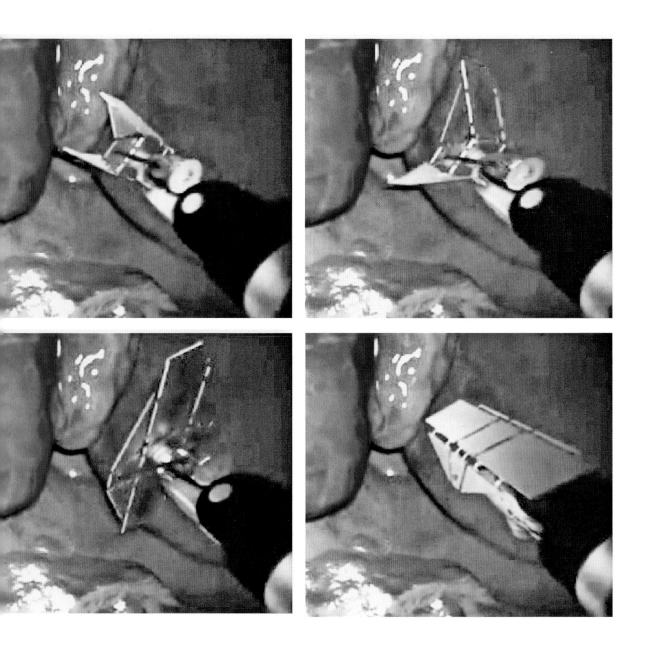

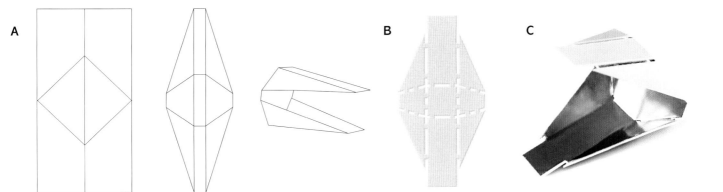

A. These seven folds create this model's titular motion. The angles between neighboring folds can be adjusted to change the gripping motion's speed and strength.
B. Material is removed along the folds so that thick, nonpaper materials can be used and still achieve the desired motion.
C. To create a flat rather than creased gripping surface, the chomper was split down the middle and rectangular pieces were inserted between the two halves.

Monolithic Pointer

Materials: Titanium
Size: about hand size

INSPIRATION: This model was not based on a specific origami model. But after the concept was developed, folded paper prototypes were used to understand the complex motion of the spherical five-bar mechanism and how it might be used to achieve independent motion in two directions. Working prototypes and the final design, however, were not made out of paper; rather, metal 3-D printing was the method chosen to manufacture the complex shape.

APPLICATION: Because the pointer is monolithic (one piece), it gains its motion through the flexing of its thin members rather than through hinges or bearings, and it doesn't need any lubrication to operate. This makes it ideal for harsh environments, such as outer space. When mounted on a spacecraft it could be used to aim a communications antenna or, due to its ability to remain stable even with applied forces, a thruster. One common solution to directional thruster control is to have several thrusters permanently arranged in several directions, so replacing those with a single thruster that can be aimed could significantly reduce the part count, complexity, and weight of these systems.

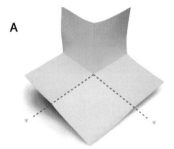

A

B

C

D

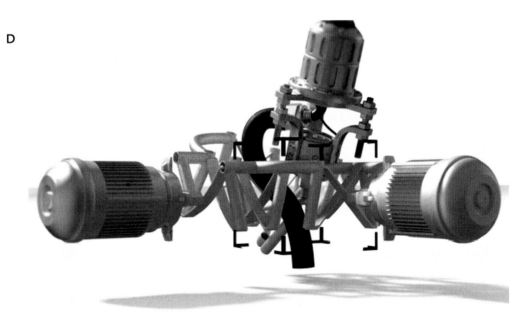

Participants: Ezekiel Merriam, Spencer Magleby, Larry Howell (BYU), with NASA Marshall Space Flight Center

A. By controlling rotation about the two axes shown here, the paper pointer can be moved as far as 90 degrees away from vertical in any direction.

B. The same two axes control motion in the titanium model, but the range of motion falls from 90 degrees off of vertical to 15. Although this range seems small when compared to paper, it is impressive in the realm of structural materials.

C. No hinges, bearings, or bushings are required for this pointer to achieve its full range of motion. This property is particularly useful in harsh environments where lubrication is difficult or ineffective.

D. This is how the pointer might look when configured to support and aim a thruster on a spacecraft. The fuel lines could run in between all of the beams and flexures to avoid pinching or blocking during motion.

Nanoinjector

Materials: Polycrystalline
Silicon
Size:1.3mmx0.6mm
Lance: 200µm long,
elevates to 45µm

INSPIRATION: Kirigami is a branch of origami in which the paper may be cut as well as folded, a practice prohibited in most traditional origami. This combination of cutting and folding can create structures and motions common in pop-up books, and this behavior was the inspiration for the nanoinjector. At the microscopic scale, traditional mechanisms are difficult to construct and operate, but this type of pop-up mechanism can be constructed relatively easily and operated consistently. Its motion is so well defined that it can rise up from the flat state and then inject DNA into a mouse egg cell with minimal damage to the cell wall.

APPLICATION: This mechanism is used for transgenic research by injecting DNA into cells. This type of research can be helpful in the study of genetic diseases and cancer research, among other things. The small scale makes the work challenging, and that is where this mechanism shines. The nanoinjector's needle is 1/100th the size of a human hair. This is ten times smaller than the alternative microinjector used for similar work, resulting in less damage being done to the injected cells.

A

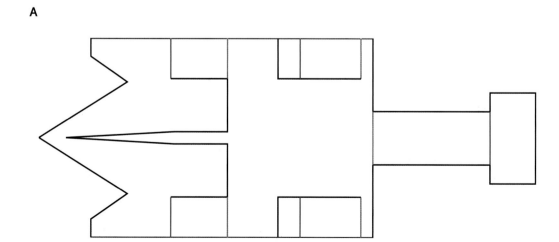

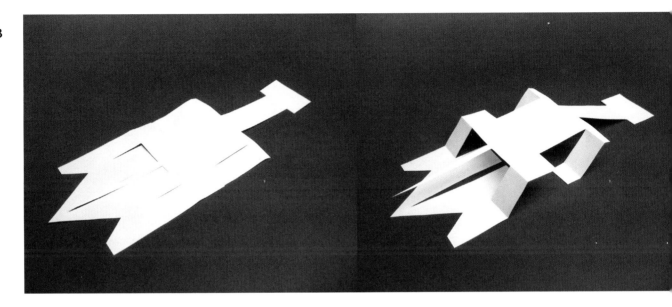

A. This simple pattern of cuts and folds gives rise to the nanoinjector's basic upward and then forward motion.

B. Similar to what is seen in pop-up books, the nanoinjector can lie flat and thin and then spring up out of the page into its active form. The height and orientation of the deployed state can be adjusted by moving some of the cuts and folds in the basic pattern.

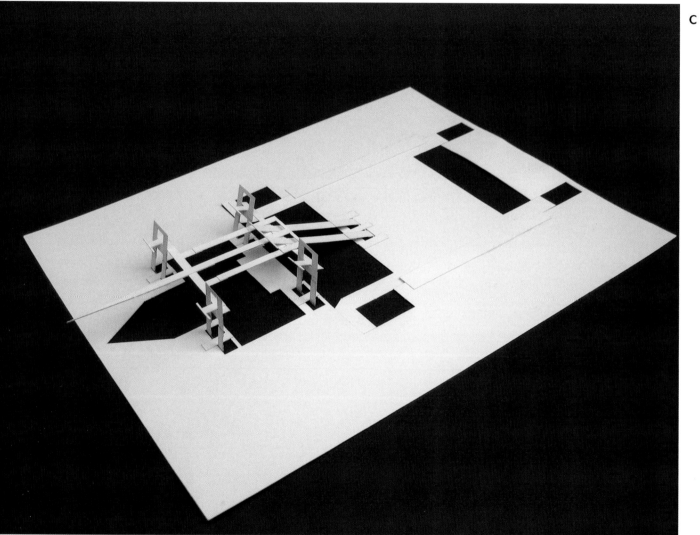

c

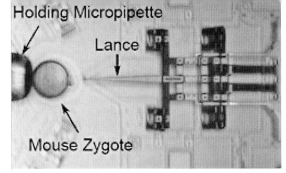

Holding Micropipette

Lance

Mouse Zygote

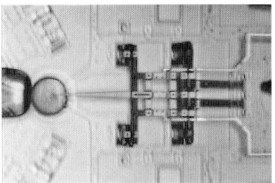

D

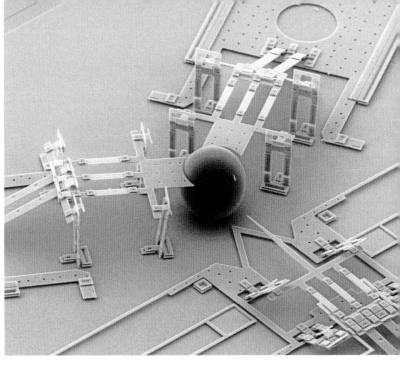

Participants: Quentin Aten, Brian Jensen, Sandra Burnett, and Larry Howell (BYU), with Crocker Ventures

C. To adapt the design for use with nonpaper materials, the folds were replaced with two interlocking layers of rigid material that slide past and through each other to replicate the motion of the paper model.

D. The nanoinjector before and during DNA injection into a mouse egg cell. High precision is required to accomplish this without causing serious damage to the cell.

Tessel Jet Pack
Backpack

Materials: Nylon fabric,
polyurethane foam
Size: 17"x11"x5"

INSPIRATION: The Tessel design was inspired by origami tessellations. A tessellation is a repeatable tiling pattern composed of one or more geometric shapes (tiles). In the case of origami tessellations, folds in the paper create the geometric tiles, and some of these patterns are infinitely repeatable in at least one direction. The ability to incorporate three-dimensionality into origami tessellations sets these apart from most other tessellation arts, which are typically created on a flat surface and restricted to two-dimensional planes.

A. Origami tessellations such as the Miura-Ori and triangulated Resch's patterns shown here provided the visual inspiration for the Jet Pack's faceted material.
B. The final pattern preserves the repeatability and crisp geometric aesthetic of origami tessellations while improving the ability to conform to different 3-D shapes.
C. Whether completely full or mostly empty, the interactions between facets give this backpack a unique and stylish look.
D. A reflective finish on the Tessel material highlights the angularity and interesting orientation of neighboring panels.

A

B

C

Courtesy of Tessel Supply.

D

Courtesy of Tessel Supply.

Participants: Aaron Puglisi, Daniel Shirley, David Morgan (BYU), with Tessel LLC and Wasatch Design Collective

APPLICATION: The faceted material was designed with the visual aesthetic of origami tessellations in mind. In addition to its clean, geometric look, the material also has a playful tactile and interactive feel. This material was incorporated into the Jet Pack, resulting in a backpack that is as fun as it is functional.

Circle/Circle Table

Materials: 1/2" poly-
propylene sheet, 1/2"
tempered glass
Size: 24" diameter;
height: 24" upright,
3" flat

INSPIRATION: The origami kaleidocycle provided the initial inspiration for the Circle/Circle Table's design. The kaleidocycle is unique in that it is capable of continuous rotation despite its lack of pins or other joints generally deemed necessary for this kind of motion. The table displays a portion of the kaleidocycle's motion as the legs transform between the flat and upright configurations.

APPLICATION: When the table is not in use, such as during storage or shipping, the legs can be folded flat and stacked with the tabletop to become a disc that is two feet across and only a few inches thick. The transforming leg assembly can be constructed with only three separate pieces if a compliant material such as polypropylene is used, but six pieces are needed when a more traditional structural material is selected.

A

A. As a kaleidocycle continuously rotates, the different faces alternate between facing away from the center and toward the center.

B. A rigid-body kaleidocycle can be constructed by joining six identical rigid links, each of which has pins at both ends that are offset from each other by 90 degrees.

B

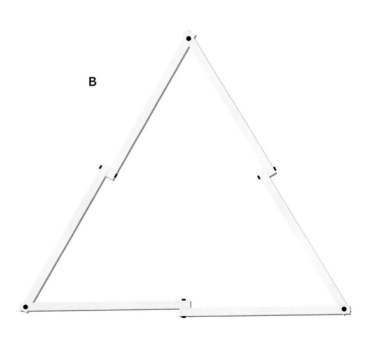

C

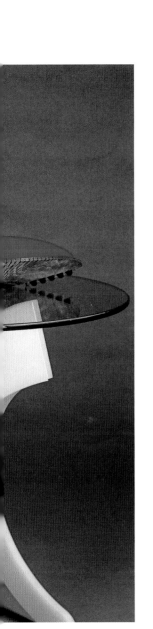

Participants: Nichole Cross, David Morgan (BYU), with Wasatch Design Collective

C. The Circle/Circle Table's legs are made of wood with six traditional rotating joints, but others have been built using polypropylene with three compliant "groove" joints as well as three traditional pin connections.

D. When laid flat, the legs have the same two-foot diameter footprint as the tabletop so the two items can be stacked into a small, portable package.

D

Plywood Hinge Bowl

Materials: Baltic birch plywood, varied surface finish
Size: 6mm thick; varied
diameter: 30cm, 40cm,
can be bigger or smaller

INSPIRATION: The plywood hinge bowls were inspired by origami's ability to take something flat and two dimensional and transform it into something 3-D. Some modern forms of origami also use rounded, curved folds rather than localized creases to give a different aesthetic to their designs. These bowls are easily converted between their flat state for storage or transportation and their round, folded-bowl shape for normal use.

APPLICATION: To enable this curved bending motion in thick, stiff materials, a modified lattice hinge was created by making the complicated series of cuts shown here. Although these hinged bowls are made from 6-millimeter thick Baltic birch plywood, they could be made from a variety of different woods, plastics, or other materials.

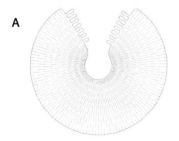

A

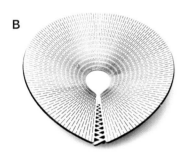

B

Participants: Nicole Cross, David Morgan (BYU), with Wasatch Design Collective

A. To create a "rounded" fold, a single crease of a given angle is replaced by a series of creases with smaller angles. The larger the number of smaller creases and the smaller their angle, the more smooth the round surface.

B. Flexible segments of stiff materials made by these kinds of small cuts are sometimes called lattice hinges, but these hinges are generally for straight bends around a single, stationary axis. The cuts here were oriented radially to get the sweeping, curving bend of the bowl.

C. The basic flat pattern can be easily modified for different bowl sizes and shapes. Several iterations were considered in selecting the final bowl design.

D. The fingers at the edge of the bowl interlock to hold it in the folded shape.

C

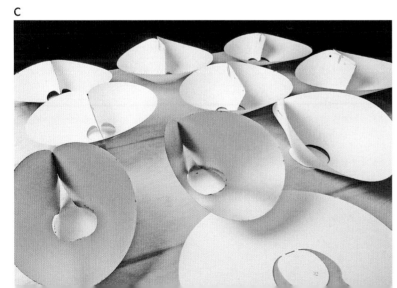

D

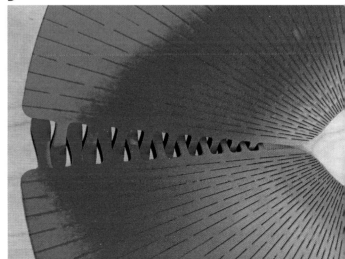

O-Retractor

Material:
polypropylene
Size: variable

INSPIRATION: Alex Ratner's magic carpet [3] provided the inspiration for the O-Retractor, a medical device for minimally invasive surgery. Simpler origami folds, such as the common V-folded origami fan, have the expandable and collapsible behavior needed, but the magic carpet's greater stiffness makes it better suited for this use. It collapses into a small package and then expands to present a large surface area for use.

APPLICATION: A retractor is used in surgery to separate organs or tissue allowing the surgeon to access the necessary body parts. Using the shapes and geometry of the magic carpet as inspiration, the O-Retractor was developed with two rigid supports separated by collapsible webbing. When collapsed the retractor can fit inside an 8-millimeter-diameter tube, and when deployed the unfolded webbing presents a large surface that can be used to move organs and other tissue to make room for other surgical instruments. Depending on the procedure, the large contact area can be easier to use and gentler on body tissues than the two gripping arms of existing retractors.

A

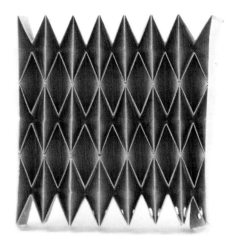

B

C

D

Participants: Bryce Edmondson, Quentin Allen, Michael McCain, John Pierce, Terri Bateman, Larry Howell (BYU)

A. Alex Ratner's magic carpet.

B. The magic carpet can be collapsed to fit inside a tube and then deployed to create a large gripping area.

C. The O-Retractor can be 3-D printed or injection molded to fit onto existing retractor tools. The rigid supports grip the retractor's arms and the webbing forms a large contact surface.

D. A latex sleeve can be fitted over the top of the retractor to increase surface area and to keep the retractor clean. When this is done, only the sleeve would need to be discarded after each procedure, and the O-Retractor itself could be reused.

A

C-Arm Shroud

Material:
0.007" thick Tyvek®
Size:
compressed
8"x3"x3"
deployed
6"x102"x0.007"

INSPIRATION: As an expandable and collapsible fold, the Miura-Ori provided inspiration for this sterile C-arm shroud for medical X-ray machines. By reorienting some of the folds and stretching some of the panels between them, the Miura-Ori was modified to wrap partway around a rectangular column while achieving a large length change in one direction but only a small change in the other.

APPLICATION: In an operating room, a sterile field around the patient and surgical area must be maintained to prevent infection. Currently, a plastic drape is used to provide a boundary between the sterile field and the extension arm of the operating room X-ray machine; however, whenever the drape moves out of the sterile field it has to be replaced, which is both time-consuming and costly. By attaching the adjustable shroud, which extends and contracts like an accordion, to the extension arm of the X-ray machine, a barrier is created between the sterile field and the nonsterile extension arm.

Participants: Levi Rupert,
Jacob Robinson, David
Richardson, Dilip Malla,
Sean Moore, Josh Lind-
mark, Anton Bowden,
Larry Howell (BYU), with
GE Healthcare

A. The Miura-Ori is recognizable on each side with simple V-folding in the middle.
B. This pattern can be made arbitrarily long for a given width. As it is stretched or compressed, the length changes much more than the width.

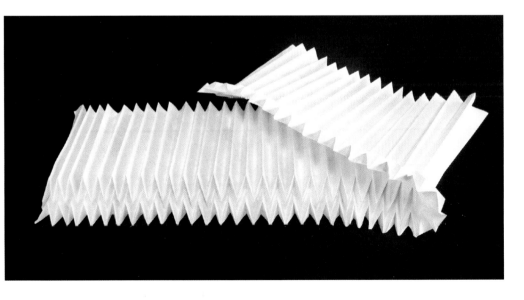

A
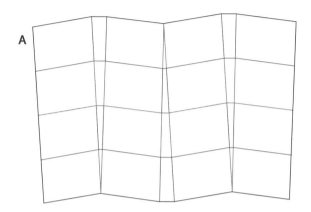

B

Backpackable Solar Array

Materials:
matboard, fabric,
monocrystalline
solar cells
Size: various

INSPIRATION: Inspired by Chuck Hoberman's fold patterns for reversibly expandable structures [4] and the deployable solar space array described earlier, this array was designed for smaller-scale, single-person use. Similar to some map folds, when deployed this array lies completely flat and when stowed it is a densely packed unit. To adapt the original design, spaces were added between panels according to the thickness of the panel material, and all panels were attached to a common membrane to preserve the layout and foldability of the array.

APPLICATION: This solar array's ability to be compactly stowed during storage or transportation and then deployed to generate energy could be useful whenever power is needed in remote, difficult-to-reach, or undeveloped areas. For example, a backpacker in a remote area could use the array to recharge a GPS© unit or satellite phone. Similarly, a military operator who doesn't have power because of a remote location or compromised infrastructure could use one of these arrays to power small electronic equipment.

Participants: Mary Wilson, Shannon Zirbel, Cory Newton, Kevin Francis, Spencer Magleby, Larry Howell (BYU)

A. The modified solar array pattern allows for sheets of finite thickness. The smaller wedge-shaped panels change size to accommodate the increasing thickness of the folded array as more thick layers are folded on top of each other.

B. This pattern can be extended in any direction as long as the small wedges keep growing to account for the increasing thickness of the folded form.

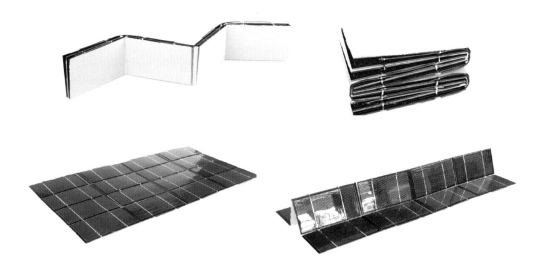

Collapsible
Camp Stove

Material:
18ga stainless steel
Folded size:
7"x8.5"x.25"
Projected Size:
7"x4.125"x5"

INSPIRATION: This collapsible stove was initially inspired by many flat-folding origami models such as Mathias van de Walle's foldable ice bucket for Veuve Clicquot. Although several specific origami patterns were considered during the development process, no single paper design inspired the final form of the stove. Instead, simple folds that open up to acute angles and then close to a flat layered form inspired the critical element of the stove—the Acutely Combined Torsional (ACT) hinge. These hinges enabled a design for nonpaper material that folds down into a flat, three-layer stack and opens up to form a freestanding structure.

APPLICATION: The folding elements needed to be integrated into the stove's design while still preserving its ability to meet critical design criteria, such as durability, fuel-type flexibility, quick cooling, and ability to stand unsupported. The ACT hinge was developed and selected for its ability to achieve the necessary deflections and still fold up into a compact form. The overall design was then optimized to maximize deployed volume and minimize folded volume. The stove is very thin when folded down but opens up and interlocks to become a stable piece of cooking gear.

A

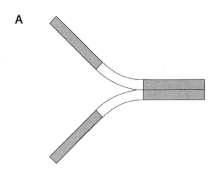

Participants: Jessica Morgan, Eric Wilcox, Todd Nelson, Nathan Pehrson, Bryce Barker, Kaleb Garlick, Terri Bateman, Spencer Magleby, Larry Howell (BYU), with QuickStove Inc.

A. An ACT hinge is created by stacking two layers of material together and fastening them at one end so that the other ends can either lie together flat or open up to acute angles. The material in this joint undergoes much less deflection than a flat sheet would to create the same angle.

B. When properly aligned and assembled, these three pieces create two acute hinges and one interlocking joint that enable the assembly to either lie flat in a compact stack or open up to stand as an isosceles triangle.

C. When deployed, a flat plate with support flanges slides into place near the bottom of the stove. This plate serves to stabilize the standing structure as well as providing a convenient place to put the stove's fuel without blocking airflow during use.

B

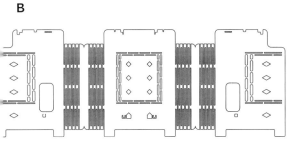

C

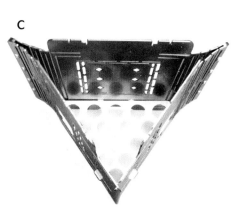

Felt
Stool

Materials: 5mm wool felt, polyester resin, urethane feet and aluminum truss
Size: 20.5"x18"

INSPIRATION: The foldable felt stool drew its inspiration from two primary sources: origami star patterns and the Flux chair by Douwe Jacobs and Tom Schouten [5]. Star patterns achieve a pleasing aesthetic by folding a single sheet, and the Flux chair is a functional piece of furniture that can be packed flat. This foldable stool blends the two ideas to create an attractive, functional stool made from a single sheet of felt that can be folded down and packed flat when not in use.

APPLICATION: To create a flat sheet that is flexible along the desired fold lines but stiff everywhere else, wool felt was selectively impregnated with resin. The resin-impregnated areas became the stiff, structural elements of the stool while the untreated felt remained flexible for folding. A small interior truss and a set of plastic feet were also designed to help keep the structure from collapsing or twisting out of shape.

A

B

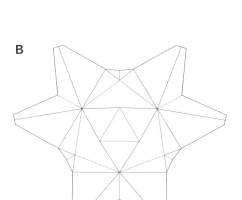

Participants: Brett Mellor, David Morgan (BYU), with Wasatch Design Collective

A. The modified solar array pattern allows for sheets of finite thickness. The smaller wedge-shaped panels change size to accommodate the increasing thickness of the folded array as more thick layers are folded on top of each other.

B. When every fold on this pattern is utilized, the flat sheet folds up into the functional stool form. When the stool is not in use, however, it can be folded into a flat, more compact form than is seen here by using just a few of the fold lines shown.

C

D

C. The fold pattern is transferred to the felt via template, then the fold lines are masked to resist the resin, which is carefully applied to achieve the desired saturation level.

D. When not in use, the interior truss and plastic feet can be removed to allow the felt sheet to be folded down into this compact triangular configuration.

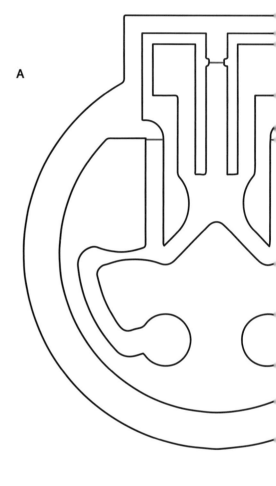

A

Lens Lift™

Materials: polymer, metal composite foil
Size: contact lens–package size

INSPIRATION: Similar to the nanoinjector, the Lens Lift™ was inspired by kirigami and pop-up books. The lifting mechanism lies flat when the package is closed and then lifts the lens up out of the saline solution as the blister pack is opened, much like how the elements of a pop-up book spring out of the page as the book is opened.

APPLICATION: A big cause of spreading infection with contact lenses is the many touch points when handling a lens. The Lens Lift™ mechanism makes using contact lenses both easier and more sanitary by holding the lens in such a way that only one finger with one point of contact is necessary to remove the lens from the package and place it on the eye.

Participants: Samuel Wilding, Holly Greenberg, Spencer Magleby, Larry Howell (BYU)

A. The Lens Lift™ mechanism can be cut from a single sheet.

B. Once cut, the Lens Lift™ is mounted in the middle of a folded sheet so that it deploys when the fold is opened.

C. The Lens Lift™ easily fits inside existing blister packs. As the blister pack is opened, the Lens Lift™ automatically deploys, lifting the contact lens out of the solution and into an easy-to-access position.

B

C

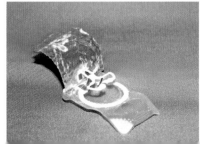

A

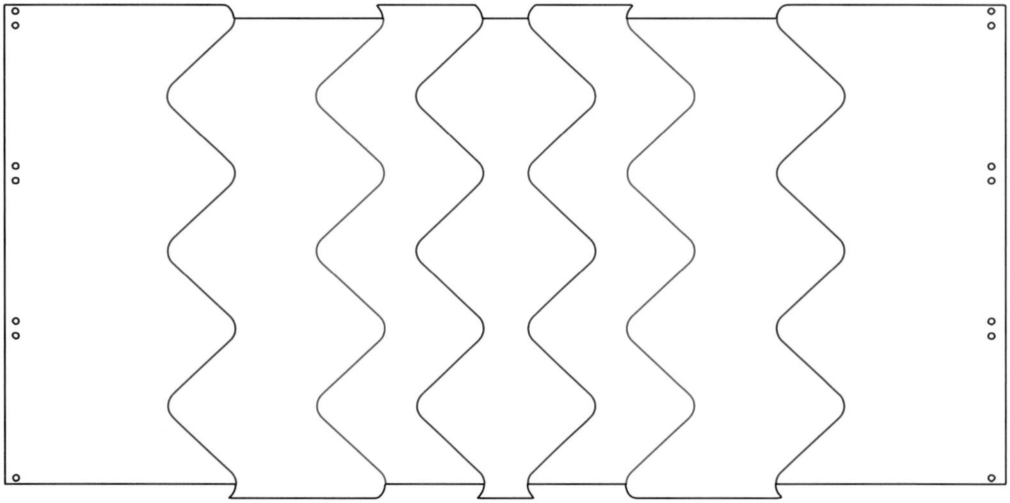

Ruffled Lamp

Materials: poly-
carbonate, 1/16"
copper-plated rod,
light fixture
Size: 8"x16"

INSPIRATION: Pleat folding, which is used in a range of different origami models, and an alligator jaw design provided the initial inspiration for this lamp, but elements of the 16th-century European ruff, or frilled collar, also influenced the final design.

APPLICATION: Each lamp is assembled from three identically cut pieces of poly-carbonate, and the curved fold lines on each piece are laser-perforated to avoid unwanted creases and bending along the delicate folds. After folding, the three pieces are hand sewn together and each of the lamp's ends are gathered together with a copper-plated steel wire.

Participants: Bryce
Barker and David
Morgan (BYU), with
Wasatch Design
Collective

A. The curved folds in the lamp's crease pattern are challenging to execute, but create a unique and attractive effect.

B. Pleat folds such as those used in this design by Matthew Gong were one source of inspiration for the lamp's design.

C. Copper-plated steel rings are used to gather the top and bottom ends of the lamp together, preserving the ruffle effect.

B

C

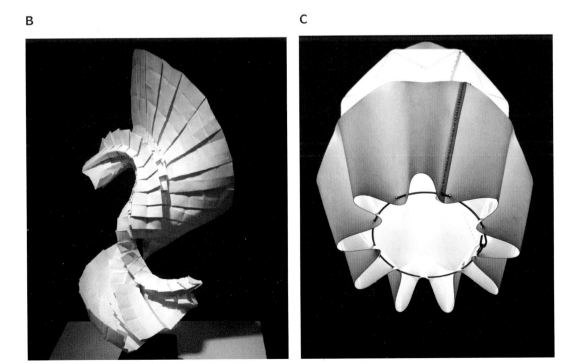

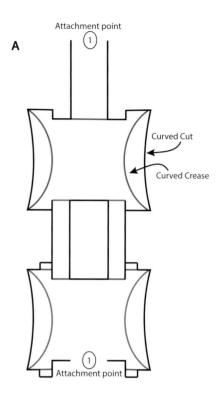

Morphing Surface

Materials: plywood, metallic glass, stainless steel
Size: 6"-15" high

INSPIRATION: Developable curved-fold patterns such as Robert Lang's Crashing Volcanoes and Elliptical Infinity [6] provided the inspiration for these morphing surfaces. Traditional origami uses straight folds to create angular models, but these designs use curved fold lines to produce smooth, flowing curves in the final forms.

APPLICATION: Curved folding makes it possible to develop complex 3-D curved surfaces using noncomplex 2-D processing methods such as punching, pressing, or laser cutting. This simplifies the process of producing objects, such as the deployable CORE joint shown here. Another benefit is that materials that typically cannot tolerate tight folds may be viable for curved folding, as local deflections are relatively small. Recent work has led to a method of cutting and thinning thicker, stiffer materials to be able to bend as these patterns require.

Participants: Todd Nelson, Larry Howell (BYU), with Robert Lang (Lang Origami)

A. The flat pattern for a CORE, or compliant rolling-contact element, appears simple compared to many origami crease patterns, but these simple lines produce a unique and useful device.

B. This model was not folded from paper but from medium density fiberboard (a board made from small wood particles) that had been specifically cut to enable it to bend without breaking.

C. The smooth, curving lines present in the flat patterns of morphing surfaces such as Robert Lang's Elliptical Infinity are strikingly different from the straight lines and hard angles of traditional origami designs.

B

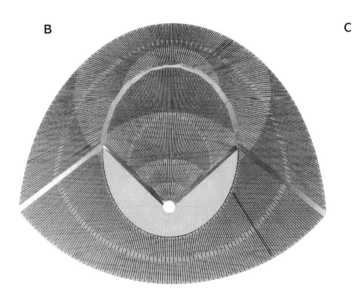

C

A

Whole Beauty Bag

Materials: leather, fabric, polyethylene
Size: 11"x 9'x 7'

INSPIRATION: This design was inspired by nature and simplified origami concepts. As the designer, Jordan Hosler, stated, "Quite directly, my work was inspired by the mountains and the simplification of the mountains into mountain and valley folds. I was looking for a connection between the way that the mountain was created and the way that it looks."

APPLICATION: Hosler went on to say, "Through this project, it was my intent to better define the way in which an object's appearance was attached to its function in the natural realm, in order to apply the same concepts to human products." In this case the design of the mountains inspired a handbag. This idea could be used for a line of bags or other products inspired by behaviors and their related functions and appearances observed.

Participant: Jordan
Parcell Hosler (BYU)

A. "Nature, as a rule, cuts out anything that is unnecessary, yet we still look at the natural world and describe it as beautiful. This is what I call 'Whole Beauty,' the idea that appearance is synonymous with behavior. When the correct aesthetic is applied to a specific function or behavior, the final product is strengthened. I learned that behavior (or the function) of the object dictated its appearance."

B. "I worked backwards, trying to replicate forms and patterns I observed in nature and then trying to understand their purpose or function. I learned quickly that it was essential to better define my area of exploration in order to make useful observations. Topography turned out to be an area that was easily observable and without any selfish motives or invisible agendas (as a living, thinking creature might have)."

C. This bag describes the movement of tectonic plates and the formation of a mountain out of flat land. The pattern of the bag folds flat and pops up into three dimensions to illustrate this movement.

B

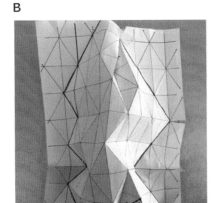

C

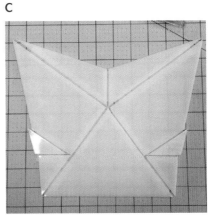

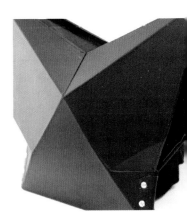

Oruga
Shelter

Materials: twin wall polypropylene sheet
Size: 33" wide, extends to 8' long

INSPIRATION: Designer Steve Puertas said: "I had the idea for this when I was stranded at the airport overnight on my way to Peru last summer. Being a college student on a budget, I could not afford to stay at a hotel. I was forced to spend the night on the floor. The end results were sleep deprivation, stress, and physical discomfort. That is when I decided to make a product that stranded travelers can rent and use to spend a more comfortable night at the airport."

APPLICATION: Oruga or Folding Guest Ambient is an origami sleeping shell designed to be lightweight, portable, and easy to use. Taking inspiration from the caterpillar, Oruga was originally made to lessen the inconvenience of being stranded at the airport due to a cancelled or delayed flight. The main goals for this project were to provide comfort, security, and privacy.

Participant: Steve
Puertas (BYU)

Extending to about 8 feet long, Oruga was made to comfortably fit one person's body and two small bags. It is made of twin wall polypropylene sheets and weighs about 18 pounds. Both the shell and the mat sections fold into a hexagon for easy transport and storage. Snap fasteners and a shoulder strap secure the folded hexagon in place. A thin sheet of foam adds comfort to the mat, and the plastic shell acts as a capable insulator. Because of its minimal design and storage capabilities, Oruga can also be used for outdoor activities or as emergency shelters.

A

Bellows

Materials: Kapton®
sheet and tape
Size: 45mm diam-
eter tube, 170mm
long

INSPIRATION: The Origami Space Bellows uses the Kresling fold pattern created by Biruta Kresling. She was inspired by biological and twisting tubes.

APPLICATION: The Origami Space Bellows is designed as a highly compressible origami bellows for harsh environments. The motive is to replace the metal bellows that are currently used to protect a Mars rover's drill shafts with a lighter, more efficient option. This bellows has a much higher compressibility than a metal bellows, which allows shortening of the heavy drill shafts. Using a foldable material also allows the metal bellows currently in use to be replaced by a lightweight space grade material.

Participants: Jared Butler, Jessica Morgan, Millie Parkinson, Nathan Pehrson, Kyler Tolman, Patrick Walton, Peter Schleede (BYU), with NASA Jet Propulsion Laboratory

A. Materials tested for the design from left to right: Mylar®, Tyvek®, Kapton®, UHM-WPE, and PFA. The fold pattern and material choice can be adapted for specific application needs. The origami bellows can be used as a protective barrier for telescopes, structural booms, or other deployable space tubes. It can even be applied to fulfill Earth-based bellows needs.

B. There are multiple origami fold patterns that can act as a bellows. The Kresling fold pattern was selected for its high compressibility and functionality. The fold pattern was optimized to fit on a Mars rover and maximize its compressibility.

C. This final version of the bellows is made from Kapton® and uses a Kresling pattern. It is designed to reach a specified stroke length and has over 95% compressibility. It consists of fourteen deployable layers. This bellows will remain stationary at both end points while rotating at all other points.

D. The Kresling fold pattern was folded in multiple space grade materials and tested for its endurance. The bellows was tested in fatigue, thermal cycling, sandstorm simulation, and high energy ultraviolet radiation.

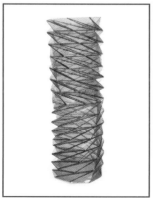

B   C   D

A   B

Biopsy
Tool

Materials: nylon,
stainless steel
Size: 38mm at 20x
scale, 10mm at 5x
scale, 2mm at final
size

INSPIRATION: The biopsy tool was developed based on the Oriceps design previously considered. The original pattern for both was Jeremy Shafer's chomper. The purpose of this project was to create a biopsy tool that would increase the tissue sample retention rate, thereby decreasing procedure time and leading to better outcomes for the patient.

APPLICATION: The idea of a mechanism cut from a single tube is interesting because it would add retention functionality to the biopsy tool while remaining simple and easy to manufacture. This idea could also be used in space applications, oil and gas drilling, and underwater exploration, among others.

Participants:
Jason Dearden,
Jared Bruton, Trent
Zimmerman, Clayton
Grames, Millie Par-
kinson (BYU), with
Intuitive Surgical, Inc.

A. Seven unique prototypes were made, which were experimentally tested in bovine liver (to simulate tissue) to aid the final concept selection. Cut efficiency, cut depth, and tissue damage tests were done.

B. The results from these tests, along with manufacturing considerations, were used to identify the best candidate of the seven concepts.

C. The compliant mechanism biopsy tool is cut from a single tube, making it simple to manufacture.

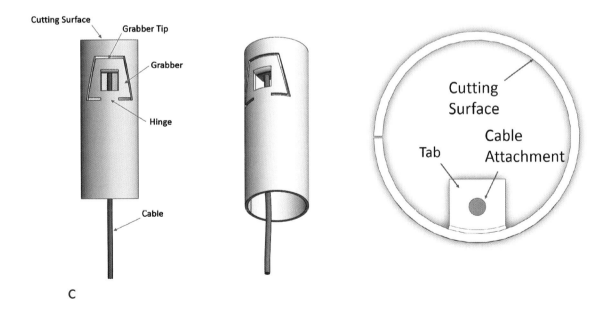

C

A   **B**

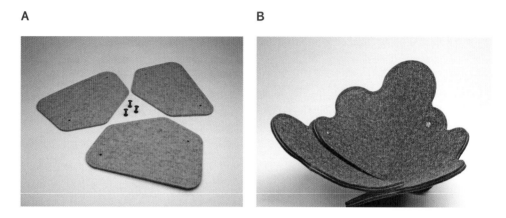

Kaleidocycle Bowls

Materials: 3mm wool felt, copper rivets, polyethylene sheet Size:12"x12"x8"

INSPIRATION: Kaleidocycles, created by Wallace Walker in the 1950s, inspired this work (see *M. C. Escher Kaleidocycles* by Doris Schattschneider and Walter Wallace). A kaleidocycle is a three dimensional ring of pyramids that has a continual twisting motion. Rather than approaching this project with the intention of making a bowl, the idea of a bowl grew out of the material exploration of kaleidocycles.

APPLICATION: The purpose of this project was to give the continual inward and outward twisting motion of a kaleidocycle a practical application by applying it to houschold goods. Early cxplorations led to a wide variety of ideas, from small, simple toys to larger-scale furniture. Some of the early iterations were able to transform from a two-dimensional to a three-dimensional object, allowing for many applications in home goods and furniture (i.e., furniture that can fold flat for easy storage).

Participants: Sam Van Slooten, David Morgan (BYU), with Wasatch Design Collective

A. The bowl is composed of three identical pieces that are connected with post and binding screws. Because these fasteners are able to be removed, the bowl can be packaged flat. The unique shape also allows the bowl to transform shapes. In one orientation, it is three sided. By rotating the bowl it becomes six sided. A second variety of the bowl allows it to change shape from a three-sided bowl to a more organic, cloud-like outline.

B. Some of the bowls have exposed plastic, making it easy for cleaning, while others have felt laminated and sewn onto both sides of the plastic, giving it a cozy, sweater-like quality. The bowl comes in a variety of color combinations, with contrasting stitching along the edge of each piece.

C. The final design used three identical pieces of felt laminated to polyethylene. Each piece was connected on each end with copper rivets. The felt and plastic allowed the piece to bend, giving it a bowl-like shape when put together. Several different iterations made using paper and metal brads were used to develop a form that had both an appealing shape and good stability. The final shape of each individual piece was designed to give the bowl two different edge shapes when rotated into each orientation, while maintaining its stability in both forms.

C

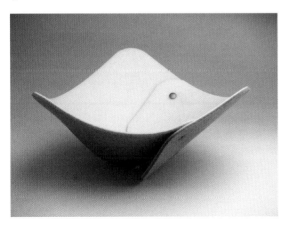

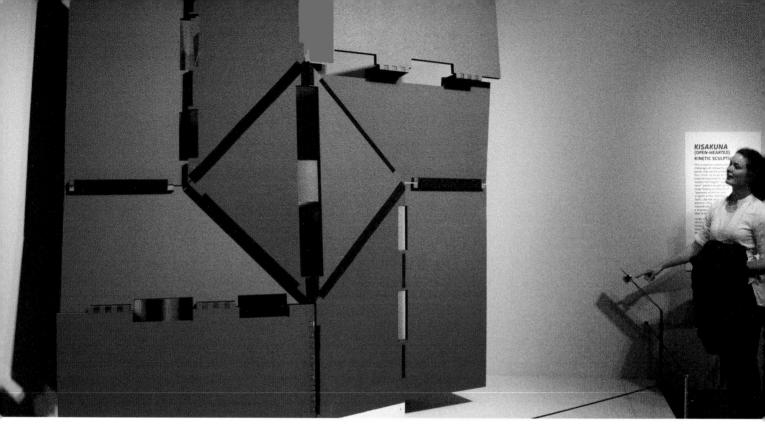

A

Kinetic Sculpture

Materials: Gator-
board, canvas
Size: from 4'x4'
to 8'x8'

INSPIRATION: This kinetic sculpture was inspired by Tomohiro Tachi's origami sculpture, as well as the square twist, a fold pattern that receives its name from the spinning motion that the square in the center experiences as the pattern is expanded or collapsed.

APPLICATION: Large kinetic sculptures require material that is stronger than paper. However, since stronger materials typically cannot crease like paper, some type of joint is required to replace the fold. And since strong-enough materials are much thicker than paper, the thickness needs to be accommodated for in revised crease patterns. The solution for this kinetic sculpture was to use a stiff foam core material with canvas joints to offset the joints so that they would lie in the same plane, and then to create clearance holes to accommodate the motion of the offset structures.

Participants: Michael Morgan, Mary Wilson (BYU)

A. Kinetic sculpture on display at the Brigham Young University Museum of Art. B. Paper square twist open and closed. The design of the origami kinetic sculpture was very much a baby-step-by-baby-step process. Initial steps included concept generation, exploration of the OPT (offset panel technique), exploration of rigid-foldable origami patterns, and exploration of potential materials. Eventually, the team settled on a simple fold pattern—the square twist. From here, small-scale models were built and experimented with and then a large-scale prototype was developed.

In a paper square twist, the square in the middle bends a little bit during the transformation between states. Since the foam core panel could not bend like paper, a joint had to be placed in the central square or else the twist could not move from one state to the other—it would be stuck as it was made.

B

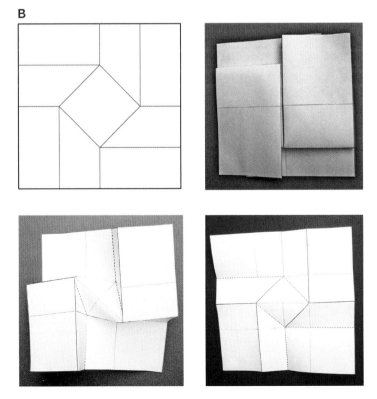

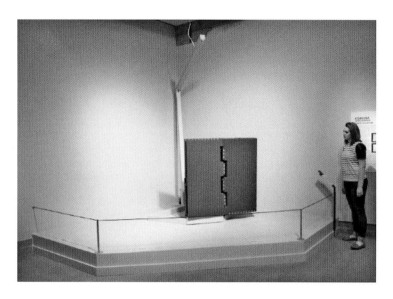

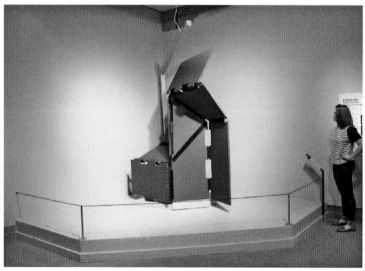
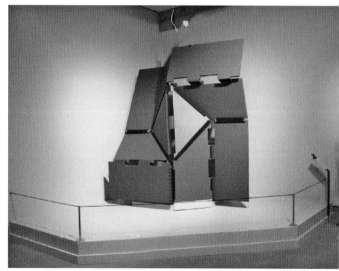

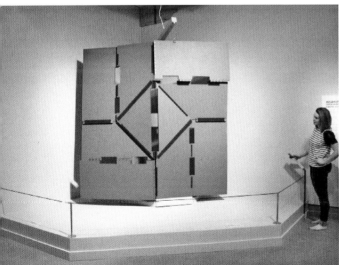

"Since the right materials played a key role in the achievement of the requirements for this sculpture, significant effort went into identifying the best material. As we narrowed in on materials and fabrication processes for the origami structure, we began to explore options for how the sculpture would be actuated and displayed in the museum. We identified the method we would use to actuate the sculpture and designed and built the electrical and software portions needed to do that. During this time we also designed and built a stand that would integrate both the sculpture and its actuation. Finally, after more than six months of work, the Kinetic Sculpture was on display in the museum."

—Michael Morgan

A

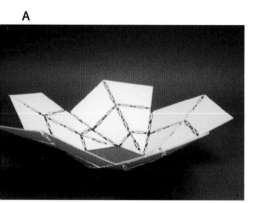

B

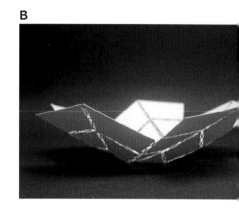

Morphing Antenna

Materials: polypropyl-
ene, adhesive
Size: 12" diameter
5" height

INSPIRATION: The origami behind the design is a flasher pattern modified to fold into a parabolic shape. This design was inspired by the origami solar panel array developed by Shannon Zirbel and used the same flasher fold pattern.

APPLICATION: The deployable parabolic antenna has possible applications for communication satellites, military in remote areas, and submarines. It would allow the antenna to fold up into a compact form for transport, then be deployed when needed.

Participants: Jessica
Morgan (BYU)

A. The antenna is based on the flasher
fold pattern with a wedge removed, and
the two adjacent wedges are adhered
together to create curvature. The antenna is made using a single sheet of polypropylene with the pattern cut out using a
laser cutter. The panels of the flasher are
attached using surrogate hinges to main-
tain a monolithic design.

B. The curvature of the antenna was
measured experimentally using a
method called Direct Linear Transformation, which is commonly used in
experimental fluids. This showed that the
curvature is approximately parabolic.

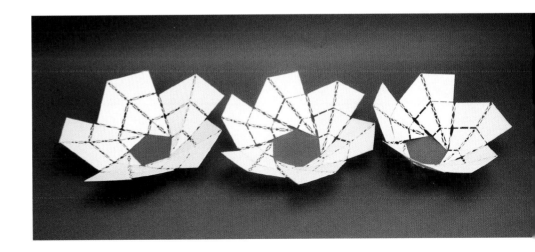

Folded
Bundt Pan

Materials: Bristol paperboard, silicone-treated parchment
Size: 12" diameter 4" height

INSPIRATION: The bundt pan began as an accordion pleat exploration and was influenced in part by the many radial origami patterns and also by various folded spans. The real inspiration came during a lunchtime idea-generation gathering when thoughts turned to dessert.

APPLICATION: After many iterations and several baking sessions, the paper pan and liner proved a success. Considerations included: size and volume of the cake, number of pleats or sections, pan manufacturability, and, of course, releasing the cake cleanly from the pan.

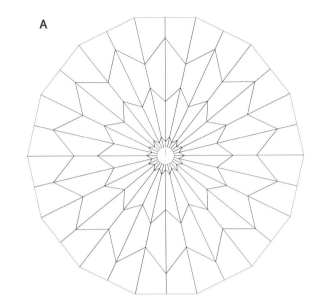

Participants: Joshua Siebert, David Morgan (BYU), with Wasatch Design Collective, and Robert Lang (Lang Origami)

A. The crease pattern developed for the bundt pan needed to be simple to produce, provide the right number of sections (pieces of cake), and have release-friendly angles.

B. The design process included many explorations and iterations to create the final bundt pan.

C. The folded silicone-treated parchment liner nests inside the Bristol paperboard pan to insure a clean release after baking. The paper pan can be reused several times with a new liner each time.

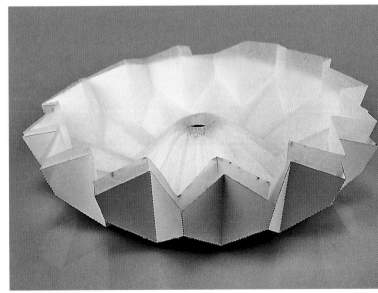

LEARNING
ACTIVITIES

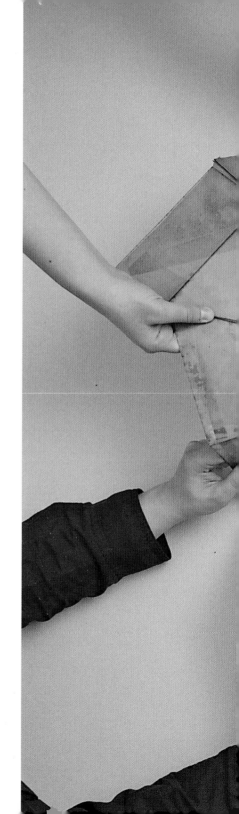

Euler's Formula

Number of vertices + number of faces - number of edges = 2

Euler's formula is one of the universal laws in origami. For any polyhedron that doesn't intersect itself, if you add the number of its vertices to the number of its faces and subtract the number of its edges, the result should always be 2. Vertex (plural vertices) is a point where multiple lines converge or come together. Edge is a straight line found in the crease pattern, and the face is an area enclosed completely by edges.

Let's try the law on the cube. A cube has 6 faces, 8 vertices, and 12 edges.

$$6 + 8 - 12 = 2$$

Now it's your turn:
How many vertices does it have?
How many faces?
How many edges?
Now calculate it by using the formula and see if the outcome is 2.

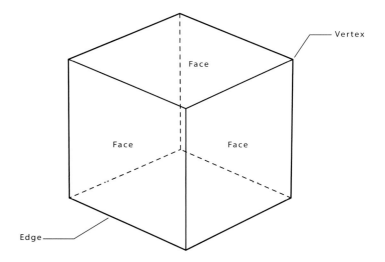

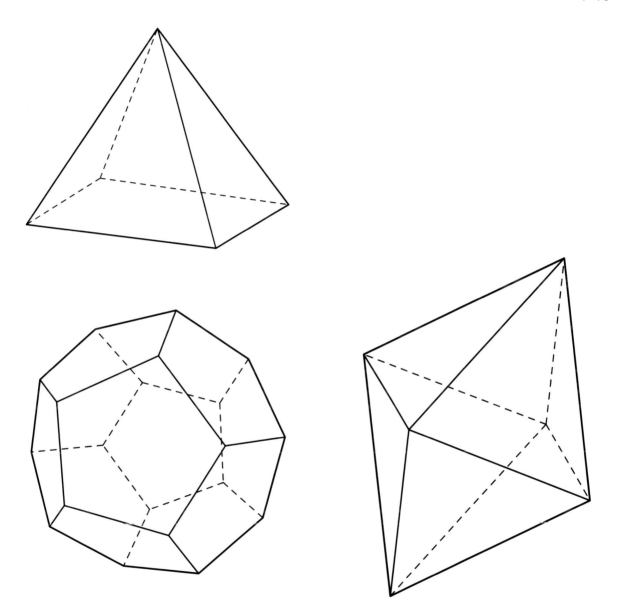

Geometric Patterns

Polygons: triangles, quadrilaterals, pentagons, and beyond

A polygon is a flat closed shape with three or more straight sides and internal angles. In origami, polygons can be created by multiple intersecting folds and many origami patterns can be partitioned into collections of panels having the same number of sides. In the examples below, we can see it is possible to identify in a single crease pattern multiple families of polygons.

Examples include:
Triangles: 3 straight sides, 3 angles
Quadrilaterals: 4 straight sides, 4 angles
Pentagons: 5 straight sides, 5 angles

Now it's your turn:
Fold, then unfold the crease and see what polygons you can identify.
What kinds are there?
How often do they show up?

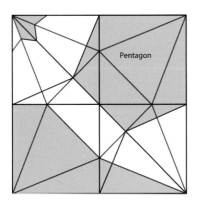

Pentagon

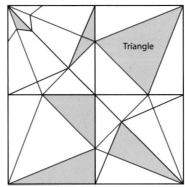

Triangle

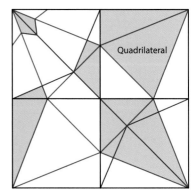

Quadrilateral

Finding Area

Area is the measurement of a surface. $A = a^2$

When it comes to space transport, finding room to pack everything is always an issue. Solar arrays require a large area in order to absorb sufficient sunlight to make enough power. So, how do you get a giant solar array into the final frontier? This is where origami comes in. The solar array designed by BYU, NASA, and Robert Lang could be the largest of them all, measuring 25 square meters open and only 2.8 square meters when stowed.

Now it's your turn:
What is the area of your square twist?
1. Measure a side when it is fully opened.
2. Plug your value into the equation:
   Multiply: $a \times a = A$ (Area)
   Write down your answer.
   (You will need it later.)
3. Fold the square twist.
4. Measure a side when it is fully closed.
5. Plug your value into the equation:
   Multlply: $s \times s = S$ (stowed area)
   Write down your answer.
6. $A - S =$ Difference

Now it's your turn:
What is the area of your flasher?
1. Measure a side when it is fully opened.
2. Plug your value into the equation:
   Multiply: $a \times a = A$
   Write down your answer.
   (You will need it later.)
3. Fold the Flasher.
4. Measure a side when it is fully closed.
5. Plug your value into the equation:
   Multiply: $s \times s = S$
   Write down your answer.
6. $A - S =$ Difference

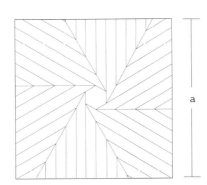

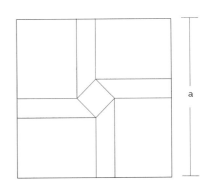

Finding Volume

Volume is the amount of space inside an object.

A water bomb is a traditional origami design that can be expanded to a 3-D "balloon." There are reasons they call it the water bomb: it will hold water and when thrown it will explode like a water balloon. The volume of a water bomb can be estimated as a cube. Measuring one of the sides we can use the formula $V=a^3$.

Now it's your turn:
What is the volume of your water bomb?
1. Measure an edge of your water bomb.
2. Plug your value into the equation:
   Multiply: a x a x a = V
   Write down your answer.

Now that you have your calculated volume, can you convert it to milliliters?
   $1 \text{ in}^3 = 16.387 \text{ ml} = 1.108$ US Tbsp.
   $1 \text{ cm}^3 = 1 \text{ ml}$
If you measured your water bomb in inches you now know why engineers, scientists, and most of the world use the metric system.

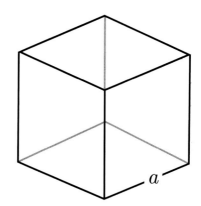

Let's find the volume of a star box.
For a pyramid, we use the equation $V = \frac{l\,w\,h}{3}$

Now it's your turn:
What is the volume of your open star box?

1. Fold up the star petals of your box and measure your base length, base width, and pyramid height.

2. Plug your values into the equation:
   Multiply: l x w x h
   Then divide your answer by 3.
   This is the volume of the whole pyramid.
   Write down your answer.

3. Fold down the star petals of your box and use the top rim as your new pyramid base.

4. Measure your new base length, base width, and pyramid height (petal length).

5. Plug your values into the equation:
   Multiply: l x w x h
   Then divide your answer by 3.
   This is the volume of the upper pyramid.
   Write down your answer.

6. Whole Volume - Upper Volume = Box Volume

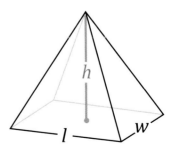

One Straight-Cut Design

Anyone who has made paper snowflakes by folding, cutting, and then unfolding a sheet of paper has seen that simple cuts in a folded sheet can create unexpected results. There is a special case of these fold-and-cut designs in which the paper is folded and then cut with only one straight, complete cut. Recent work by Demaine and O'Roarke[7] has shown that the one-cut method can be used to create any polygonal shape. Simple one-cut designs were in use long before these complex methods were developed, however. In his book *Paper Magic* [8], Harry Houdini shows how to fold and cut a five-point star. Going even further back, there are stories told of how

Betsy Ross convinced George Washington to use a five-point star on the American flag by showing how easy it was to produce by folding a sheet several times and cutting it once [9]. The following pages will present the one-cut patterns for a five-point star, and a block Y letterform.

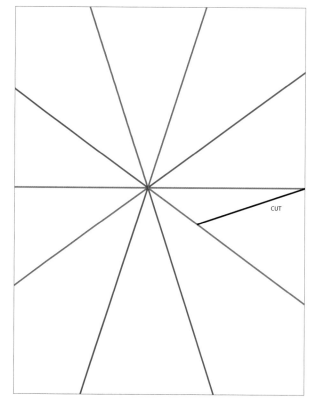

CUT

Betsy Ross Star:
1. Start by folding the paper in half along the line as shown.
2. Fold along the other lines as shown.
3. When folding it together, make sure the cut line is on the top.
4. Cut along the black line. Make sure to cut through all the layers.
5. Unfold the small piece; there's your five-pointed star.

1
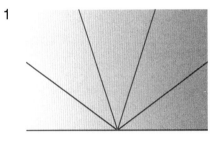

2
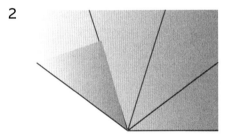

3

4
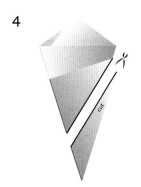

5

The Block Y:

1. Crease along all lines as indicated using the pattern on the right.

2. Using the folds as guides, collapse the sheet toward the vertical centerline, as shown.

3. Once the sheet has been collapsed along the vertical centerline, it will look like this when laid down on its side. Make the last fold through all layers along the center of the sheet.

4. Make one straight cut along the line that runs through A and B. Make sure to cut through all of the folded layers.

5. After making the straight cut, there are two pieces of folded paper. Unfold the piece that has A and B printed on it.

6. Here is the block Y.

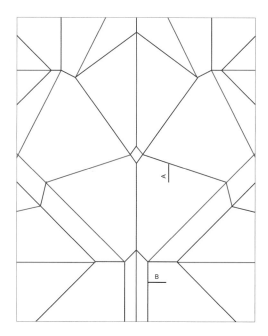

1

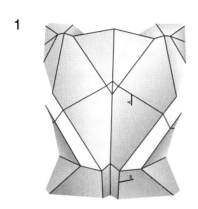

2

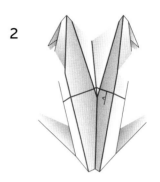

3

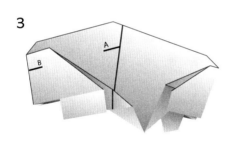

4

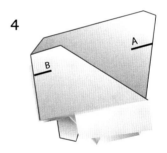

5

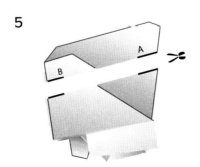

6

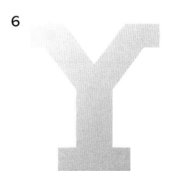

Thick
Square Twist

The kinetic sculpture shown here is made of a much larger square of material than just a regular piece of paper, and it is made of a material that is an entire inch thick. Try folding that! It turns out that once materials start to get thicker than paper, it becomes harder and harder to fold an origami pattern. Scientists and engineers have looked into this problem and have come up with a few methods for "folding" thick materials. Actually, in most of these methods, the materials aren't folded at all; rather, they are joined by some kind of hinge or joint.

In our kinetic sculpture, the thick panels were cut out individually, stacked as they would be in the paper model, and then we added offsets to extend the fold edges back to where they would be on the paper model. After that, we used fabric to create the hinges. This method is called the offset panel technique. Can you think of any other ways to make origami models with thick materials? Try cutting each panel from this pattern out of a piece of thick cardboard and see what you can come up with.

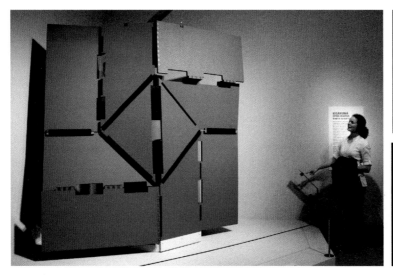

Now it's your turn:

What will your kinetic sculpture look like?

1. Print or copy the fold pattern onto a piece of paper.

2. Cut along the outer edges of the square pattern.

3. Following the guidelines for mountain/valley folds, crease the square twist pattern.

4. Take two opposite corners and push them toward the middle, letting creases fall in their orientation.

5. The large square should fold down into a smaller square in the middle.

6. Draw, paint, or write something (a cartoon character, a logo, a scene, etc.) on the face of the folded pattern.

7. Now the fun part—open the square twist pattern (you'll see your drawing be split in half and move to opposite corners) and complete the drawing or phrase on the unfolded square.

Watch the transformation as you open and close your kinetic sculpture. If it is folded correctly, you can push the sides in and out and see the square shrink and expand.

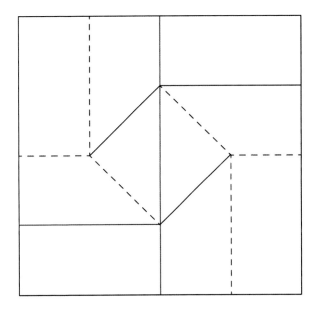

Oriceps

Discretization means to approximate something by breaking it up into smaller parts. You see examples of discretization every day when you look at images on a TV, computer, or phone screen. Images with smooth curves are really made up of small squares of color, or pixels that approximate the real thing. Examples of this are computer graphics, 3-D printing, signal processing, numerical solutions, and ADC or Analog to Digital Converter. In computer animation, a 3-D surface is broken down into little triangles to help with computing. Even drawing stick figures when starting out in art is an act of discretization. The spherical forms at right are examples of a discretized image. 3-D printing, an increasingly popular method of manufacturing, breaks down 3-D geometry in discrete layers. Shapes are made by laying material down one layer at a time. With greater resolution, or the thinner the layers are, the model will be higher quality with smoother surfaces when finished.

The chomper and oriceps are discretized fold patterns based on the curved pattern shown here. Try folding all three patterns. What differences do you see in folding and making these models move? In this example the pattern with curved creases is the example of the smoothest fold. To fold this one, you only approach a curve by creasing it in many little parts. The oriceps and chomper patterns are made up only of straight creases. This makes them easier to fold. The curved pattern takes a bit more effort to make a good crease, but it holds its form better and is easier to actuate.

With this particular model, the inspiration worked the other way. It started with the chomper model and went to the oriceps. From there we were able to try it with curved folds and have been able to study further the benefits of the curved creases. The design process refined the model rather than discretize it. Discretization is important in finding the size and shape needed for the final curved-crease model. The chomper can be used to find the right dimensions needed.

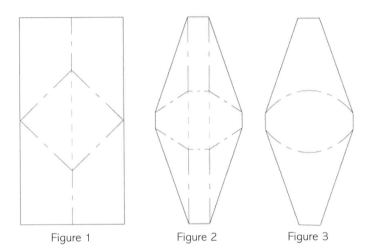

Figure 1   Figure 2   Figure 3

Now it's your turn:

1. Copy and print the images.

2. Cut out the shapes on the black lines.

3. First, take the design with curved folds (Fig. 1).

4. Crease by making small pinches along the curve.

5. Make it "chomp" by squeezing on the sides with two fingers, making the mouth open and close.

6. Next, try the middle model with the two parallel creases (Fig. 2).

7. Fold it according to the crease pattern. To make it easier, start out with all the mountain folds and make the valley folds last.

8. This will open and close just like the other model.

9. Finally, fold the last model (Fig. 3).

10. Again, start with the mountain folds and fold the valley folds last. To make this one open and close, use two hands—it will look different from the other two.

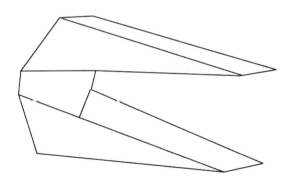

Nanoinjectors

This activity provides the steps to cut out and fold a scale model of the nano-injector. The real nanoinjector (page 18) uses electrical currents to activate the injector delivering DNA to a cell. The point is so small it is 1/100th the size of a human hair! Since the point is not hollow like a needle, it is called a lance. The pop-up design allows the nanoinjector to lie flat, and then it can be "popped up" in order to inject DNA into a cell. This design follows a kirigami model, which unlike traditional origami, allows for cutting in addition to folding. This model is about a 150:1 scale of the real model. Make this model out of cardstock or construction paper to make it stiffer. You may also make a water bomb (page 76) and simulate the actual working nano-injector injecting into a cell.

Now it's your turn:
1. Copy the pattern onto paper.
2. Use scissors to carefully cut on the solid lines. (Warning: Do not cut the dotted lines; you will need to fold these. Also, this model is meant to stay attached to the page so be careful not to cut it out of the paper.)
3. Crease on the lines as shown (mountain and valley).
4. Push at the back of the model with your finger (where it says "push").
5. Your model should pop up out of the paper, just like the real nanoinjector does.

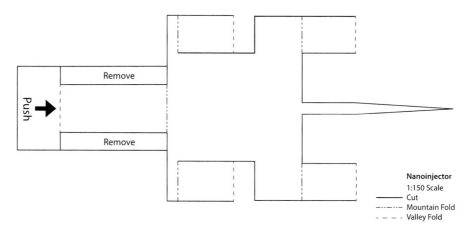

Nanoinjector
1:150 Scale
——— Cut
-------- Mountain Fold
- - - - Valley Fold

Modularity

A module is a 3-D object made up of multiple pieces. Although each piece is usually the same, there are always exceptions. One example is a soccer ball made up of many similar patches of material. Another example is the International Space Station. Each piece of the International Space Station has a different function, but each piece needs to fit with another piece. Since cargo space is limited on a shuttle, modules of the International Space Station had to be sent individually and assembled in space.

Now it's your turn:

1. You will need 3, 6, 12, or 30 pieces of square paper, depending upon the desired Sonobe (can be varied to really any value).

2. Using the instructions on the following pages, fold twelve Sonobe units. Each should look like (A).

In this activity you will make what is called a Sonobe module, which is one of many units that can be used to build modular origami. Each piece is the same and is created with pockets and tabs so that several pieces can be connected to form a 3-D object. Although there are many variations for folding the pieces of this Sonobe module, only one is shown here. Once you have folded the modular pieces, you can try constructing different 3-D shapes with the same pieces.

3. Take three units and fit them together, forming a pyramid to look like (B).

A

B

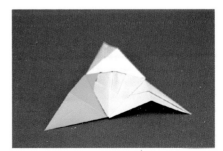

1. Place your square in front of you and fold it in half, making a horizontal crease in the middle of your square.

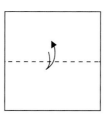

2. Now fold each half of the two rectangles you just made in half once again.

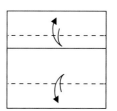

3. Take the lower left corner and fold it up to the bottom-most crease.

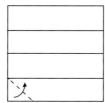

4. Rotate paper 180 degrees and repeat Step 3.

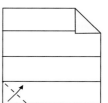

5. Now take the long edge of the triangle you just made in the corners of your paper and fold it up to meet the bottom-most crease.

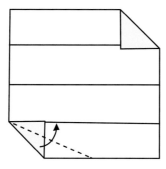

6. Rotate paper 180 degrees and repeat Step 5.

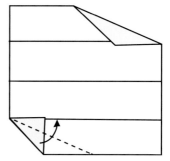

7. Now fold the top and bottom rectangle along the folds you made in Step 2 (these are lines AB and CD).

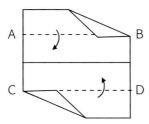

8. Now taking the bottom right corner (E), fold it up so that it meets point (F)—this also means that the right edge will lie along the top edge.

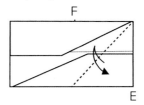

9. Rotate paper 180 degrees and repeat Step 8.

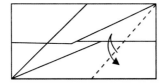

10. Now refold the corners according to the creases made in Steps 8 and 9, but tuck them under the flaps that were made in Step 7.

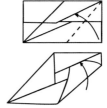

11. Your Sonobe units should now look something like this:

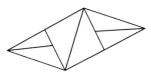

12. Next, flip the unit over so that you see the back side.

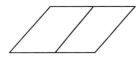

13. Take the right side of the unit and fold it to the left so that you make the vertical crease shown in the image below.

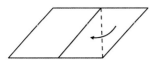

14. Rotate the figure 180 degrees and repeat Step 13. Your unit is now finished. Making multiple units will allow you to make a 3-D model (size of the model will depend on how many units you make).

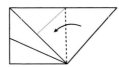

ISS Configuration

As of May 2011 (ULF6 - STS-134)

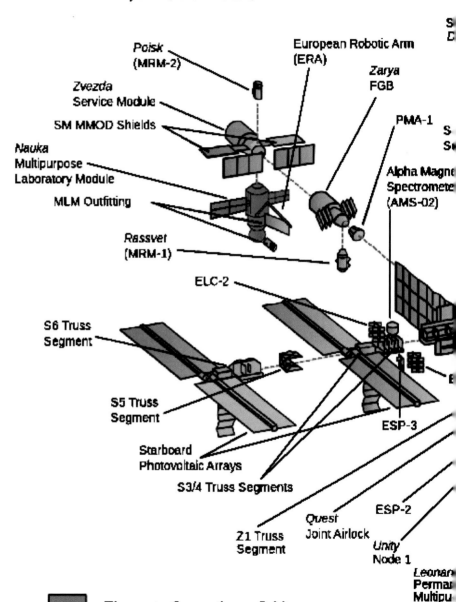

Poisk
(MRM-2)

European Robotic Arm
(ERA)

Zarya
FGB

PMA-1

Zvezda
Service Module

SM MMOD Shields

Alpha Magne
Spectromete
(AMS-02)

Nauka
Multipurpose
Laboratory Module

MLM Outfitting

Rassvet
(MRM-1)

ELC-2

S6 Truss
Segment

S5 Truss
Segment

ESP-3

Starboard
Photovoltaic Arrays

S3/4 Truss Segments

ESP-2

Quest
Joint Airlock

Z1 Truss
Segment

Unity
Node 1

Leonar
Perma
Multipu
Module

The ISS Configuration graphic was obtained online and is the created property of NASA and therefore public domain.

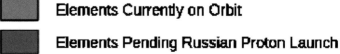

Elements Currently on Orbit

Elements Pending Russian Proton Launch

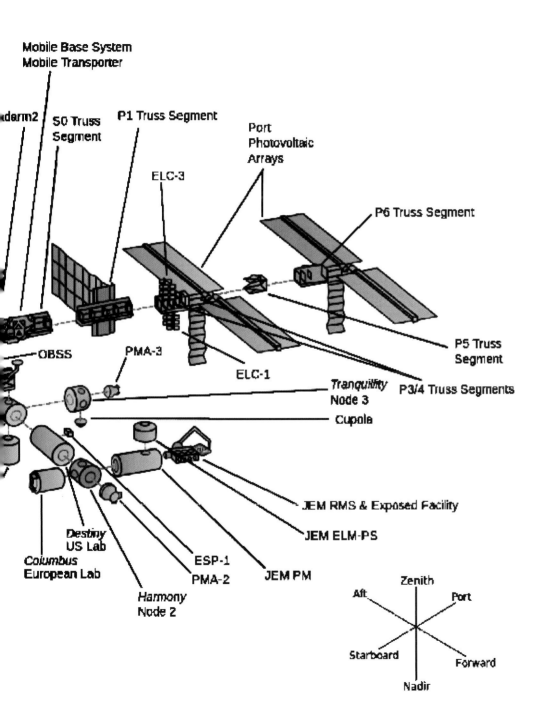

Mobile Base System
Mobile Transporter

...darm2

S0 Truss
Segment

P1 Truss Segment

Port
Photovoltaic
Arrays

ELC-3

P6 Truss Segment

P5 Truss
Segment

OBSS

PMA-3

ELC-1

Tranquility
Node 3

P3/4 Truss Segments

Cupola

JEM RMS & Exposed Facility

JEM ELM-PS

Destiny
US Lab

ESP-1

JEM PM

Columbus
European Lab

PMA-2

Harmony
Node 2

Zenith

Aft

Port

Starboard

Forward

Nadir

Angular Measurements

Every intersection of lines within a crease pattern has a number of angles that surround a vertex. If you label these angles, then the sum of the even numbered angles will add up to 180 degrees. The sum of the odd numbered angles will also add up to 180 degrees.

Let's say that angles 2, 3, 5, and 6 are each 45 degrees, while angles 1 and 4 are 90 degrees.

Add the even ones together:

45°+90°+45° = 180°

Now add the odd ones:

90°+45°+45° = 180°

You can see that it works.

Now it's your turn:

1a=70°, 2a=65°, 3a=45°, 4a=45°, 5a=65°, 6a=70°

Try adding them altogether as we did before.

Does it hold true for the crease pattern you folded?

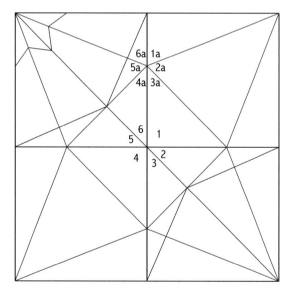

Developable Surfaces

A developable surface is a shape that can be formed by folding a flat pattern into a final formed shape without any distortion or wrinkling. In many cases where folding from a flat state to a final position is desirable, using developable surfaces makes manufacture and use much simpler. Some examples of developable surfaces are cones, cylinders, and tangent surfaces. The Plywood Hinge Bowl, which is a truncated cone, is an example of a useful curved shape that can be created from a flat sheet. When curved surfaces are needed in places like architecture, developable surfaces decrease construction costs because they do not have to be deformed to take their curved shape. Developable surfaces can be created by using curved creases as in origami patterns. Designing with developable surfaces is an exciting area of study for creating mechanisms that can fold from flat to some final curved form with minimal effort.

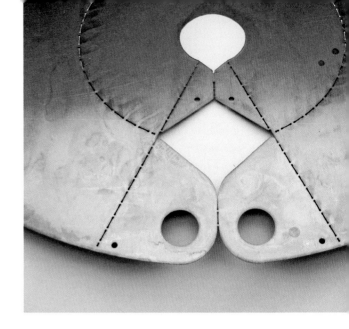

Now it's your turn:

Print out two copies of the activity print-out. From one copy, cut out the flat patterns given (cylinder, cone, Mobius strip, spherican). Leave the other copy uncut for a later step.

Cylinder and Cone:

1. Fold the cylinder, taping it together (lines A and A).

2. Fold the cone, taping it together (lines A and A).

3. Place the uncut copy of the printout on a hard surface.

4. Roll the cylinder and cone along their uncut paper pattern counterpart, lining up the taped seam with the corresponding flat pattern line. Notice that because they are developable, every part of each shape will touch the surface at some point along the roll, and they will trace out their flat patterns exactly.

5. Cut the top off of the cone to make it look like the plywood hinge.

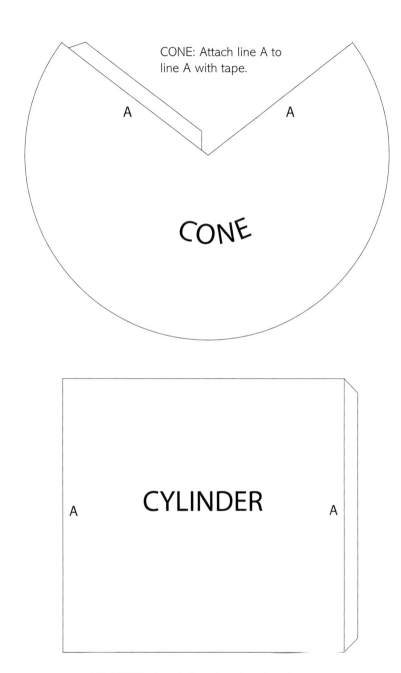

CONE: Attach line A to line A with tape.

A   A

CONE

CYLINDER

A   A

CYLINDER: Attach line A to line A with tape.

MOBIUS STRIP

Mobius Strip:
1. Cut out pattern of Mobius strip.
2. Twist it almost to a circle.
3. Rotate one end 180 degrees.
4. Attach ends with tape.
5. Trace a line with a pencil or pen along the Mobius strip. Notice that the line will appear both on the inside and on the outside of the strip before you are done.

Sphericon:

1. Fold the sphericon, taping small pieces of tape to the curves as they are placed together.
2. Tape curves A to A.
3. Tape curves B to B; this may be a bit harder than A to A.
4. Lines C and C should line up and can then be taped together.
5. Roll the sphericon along its uncut pattern counterpart (from the uncut printout placed on the table).

If it is rolling the wrong way, try lining up curve A with the curve on the sheet and make sure line C touches line C. Then try rolling it again. Notice how it rocks back and forth from side to side while rolling, and notice that like the cone and cylinder, every part of it will touch the surface at some point during the roll. It will exactly trace out its flat pattern. The sphericon is a special category of developable surface called a "rolling developable." More complex developable surfaces such as the sphericon are often made of combinations of the more basic shapes such as cones and cylinders.

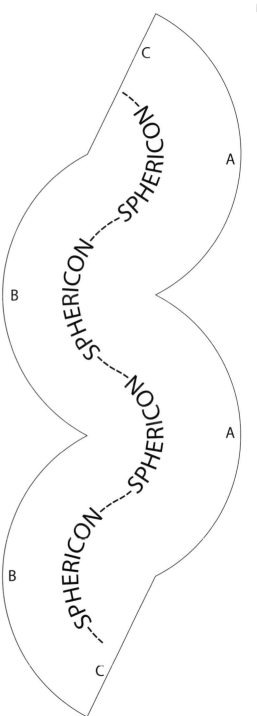

Pop-Up

Everyone has seen a pop-up book. These books allow a 3-D image in the book to "pop" out of the page and refold flat once the page is turned. There are many methods to produce these pop-up images. In fact, engineering students used the pop-up method to invent a contact case that allowed an easier way to take the lens out of the package. The lens would lift right out of the case on its own! What other ways could you use a pop-up-like mechanism? Packaging? Robotic devices? How about a ketchup bottle lid? Can you use different angles to make triangles that pop out? Four methods to produce pop-up images are shown in these instructions, and the fifth activity is an opportunity to try one with your own design. These designs use kirigami, which allows for folding and cutting.

Now it's your turn:
Print a copy of the activity printouts.

Activity A:
1. Fold page in half using the mountain fold line as your guide (ignore all other fold lines for now).
2. Cut along solid lines from the fold to the end of the line.
3. Fold each flap back and forth (mountain and valley) to make it easier to pop out later.
4. Open page and reverse fold the flap on given valley fold lines.
5. Use the given crease pattern to let each crease fold into its designated assignment (mountain or valley).
6. As the paper is opened and closed the flap will become a pop-up tab or box.

Activity B:
1. Fold page in half using the mountain fold line as your guide (ignore all other fold lines).
2. Cut along the solid lines that start at the crease you just made. (Do not cut the one line that does not start on the crease.)
3. With the longest flap, fold up along the bolded mountain fold line.
4. Cut the solid line from that fold to the end of the line. (Make sure to cut through all layers of paper.)
5. Fold each flap back and forth along fold lines.
6. Open up page and reverse fold the tabs.
7. Use the given crease pattern to let each crease fold into its designated assignment (mountain, valley).
8. As the paper is opened and closed it should look like a Christmas-tree-like pattern with each level alternating mountain and valley folds.

A

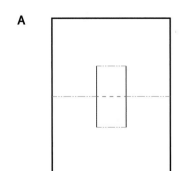

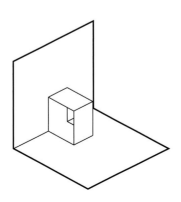

B

C

D

Activity C:

1. Fold page in half along bolded mountain fold line. (Ignore all other fold lines.)
2. Cut along the solid line from the crease to the corner of the pattern.
3. Fold the two flaps created along the mountain fold lines making two triangular flaps.
4. Cut the smaller solid line from the crease to the corner of that pattern.
5. Fold the smaller flaps along the mountain fold line similar to Step 3.
6. Unfold all the flaps and open up the paper.
7. Reverse fold and fold creases, making sure they fall into their designated pattern (mountain and valley).
8. As you open and close this pattern you will see a frog open and close its mouth and eyes.

Activity D:

This activity is the same as Activity A except that you choose the pattern to use. You can use the faded pattern to make a cityscape or make your own design.

Hyperbolic Paraboloid

In this activity, students will create a corrugated hyperbolic paraboloid shape through a radial square origami pattern. A hyperbolic paraboloid is the shape of a Pringles® chip (A), and is sometimes called a saddle because of its shape. It is also found in architecture in structures such as outdoor pavilions and even in some church buildings. The name hyperbolic paraboloid is derived from the two cross sections, one called a parabola and the other called a hyperbola (B). Corrugation is used to strengthen a flat piece of paper and is done by folding it back and forth, similar to the sheet on the inside of cardboard (C, D). This zigzag technique allows a support much stronger than one that is straight and flat. As this up-and-down pattern is applied to paper, the creases want to remain straight while the model folds in.

A

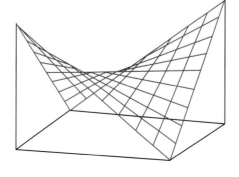

B

C

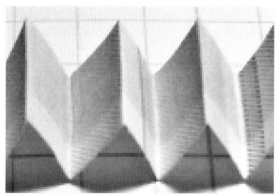

D

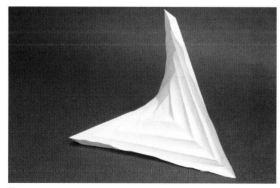

E

Now it's your turn:

1. Copy the pattern from the next page onto paper.

2. Cut out pattern from the rest of the sheet.

3. Fold in half diagonally along the fine-dotted lines and unfold. Make these creases sharp, as they will be important as a guideline for the other creases.

4. Repeat Step 3 on the other fine-dotted lines.

5. Crease the mountain folds. Make sure you do not crease all the way across the paper but stop at the diagonal crease you have already made.

6. Repeat Step 5 with the valley folds. Don't worry if the model doesn't form yet; some of the mountain folds may unfold when you crease the valley ones.

7. With all the creases made, work from the outside in, and help each crease fall into shape (valley or mountain).

8. It helps to push in from the center of each edge of the square and make the creases collapse like a paper fan.

If done correctly the paper will look like a hyperbolic paraboloid (E).

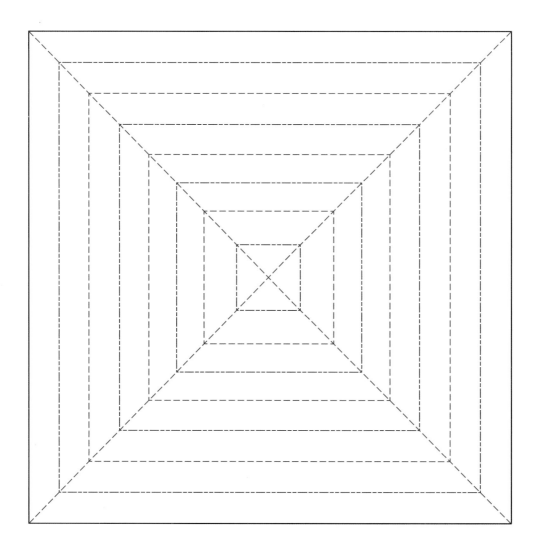

Bellows

The compressibility of a bellows is how compact it can become relative to its full length—the compressibility can be determined by measuring the compressed height and the expanded height. Depending on the thickness of materials used in construction, well-designed and constructed bellows can achieve over 90% compressibility. Both compressibility and lightness of weight are important in space applications since storage is limited and the heavier the load, the more expensive it is to send into space (roughly $10,000 per pound of payload). The bellows pictured below are designed for use on a Mars rover drill. The key to the drill's success lies in its ability to extend and retract on delicate shafts, which may become jammed, ablated, or disabled from environmental factors like dust storms and thermal fatigue. The bellows protect the delicate equipment on a Mars rover from damage caused by the environment. Bellows are also used in various applications ranging from musical instruments (like accordions) to safety guards on machines. There are several different designs of origami bellows, including the accordion pattern, Kresling pattern, and the Tachi-Miura Polyhedron. Below is the Kresling fold pattern, which is a tessellation that twists to collapse.

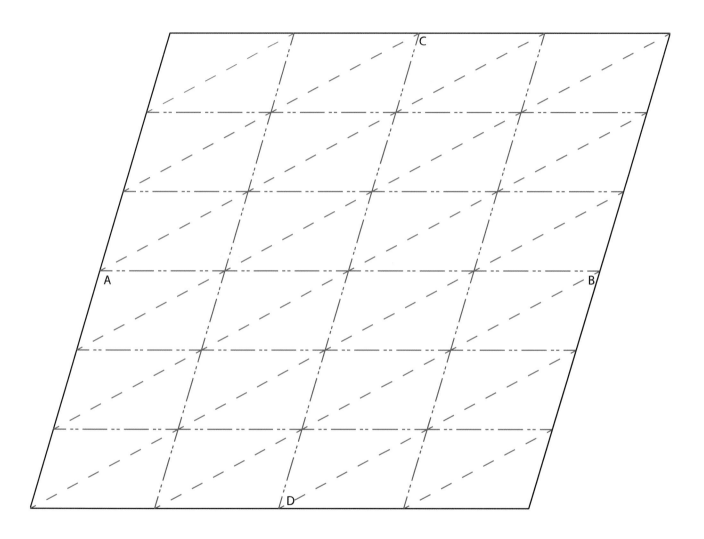

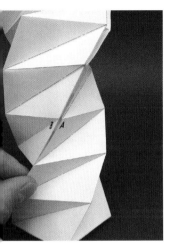

1

Figure 2

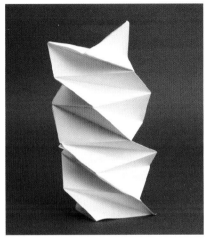

Figure 3

Figure 4

Now it's your turn:

1. Copy the origami bellows fold pattern.
2. Cut out the fold pattern from the rest of the sheet.
3. Crease all of the mountain folds.
4. Crease all of the valley folds.
5. Gently twist and close bellows, allowing the creases to fall into their orientation; It may be helpful to twist one layer at a time.
6. Continue twisting and collapsing so edge A and edge B line up but do not overlap (Fig. 1).
7. Locate remaining edges in bellows and tape together (Fig. 2).

8. The bellows can be compressed by twisting and pushing the ends together; it can be extended by twisting the opposite way (Figs. 3, 4).
9. Measure the compressed height and extended height of the bellows.
10. Calculate the compressibility by subtracting the compressed height from the extended height and dividing the total by the extended height; multiply by 100 to get a percentage.
Compressibility= $(he\text{-}hc)/he \times 100$, where he is the extended height and hc is the compressed height.

Additional challenges:

Fold another bellows, but this time match up sides C and D and tape them together. This will create a six-sided bellows with four levels. Measure and calculate the compressibility of this new bellows. Did the compressibility increase or decrease?

You can also try folding bellows using thicker materials, such as cardstock or construction paper. After folding bellows with thicker materials, measure and calculate the compressibility to see how material thickness affects compressibility.

D-CORE Catapult

Is there anything more exciting than launching an object into the air using a catapult? In this activity, you get to make a Jacob's ladder-like joint called the Deployable Compliant Rolling-Contact Element, or D-CORE. You will see how the location of the axis of rotation changes througout the D-CORE motion compared to a joint with a stable axis of rotation. The axis of rotation of a joint is the line about which two bodies rotate. For example, the hinge of a door is located on the axis of rotation of a door. With a traditional door hinge, a pin defines the axis of rotation. But with a D-CORE joint the axis of rotation moves during the joint's motion along the curved surface of the cylinders. The D-CORE, which will form the joint of the catapult in this activity, consists of two cylindrical surfaces that roll over the top of one another and are held together by bands. A Jacob's ladder toy uses this same config-uration with flat plates rather than cylin-drical surfaces.

Now it's your turn:

For this activity you will need:

tape

scissors

tongue depressor

(or Popsicle® stick)

Catapult Base

Scale bucket to fit tongue depressor or Popsicle® stick.

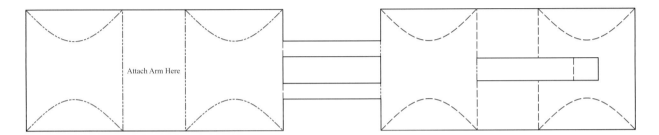

Attach Arm Here

Projectile Bucket

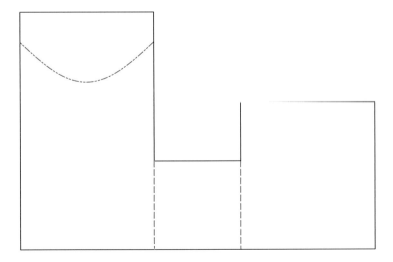

1. Copy the pattern for the D-CORE catapult.

2. Cut along the black solid lines of the catapult base, including the ones in the middle of the pattern.

3. Crease the folds with the designated mountain and valley fold patterns. Trace the curved folds with a pen or bone folder to help them fold easier.

4. Roll the curved creases into each other to make the cams of the joint (A). Secure the edges with tape (B).

5. Place the middle band through the two outer bands and tape the end to the opposite cam to create the Jacob's ladder-like joint (C).

6. Attach a tongue depressor or Popsicle® stick to spot labeled "Attach Arm Here" on the catapult base with tape. Leave about 2 centimeters of the stick overhanging the joint on one side.

7. Cut out the projectile bucket for either the tongue depressor or Popsicle® stick size depending on what you are using for the catapult arm.

8. Crease the bucket pattern with the given valley and mountain folds (D).

A   B   C

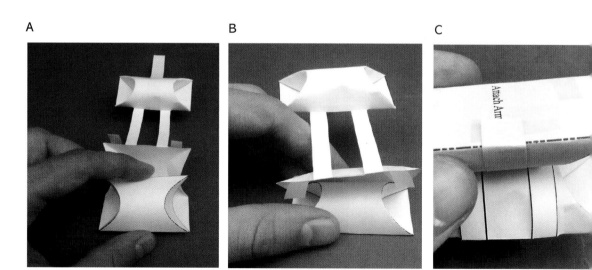

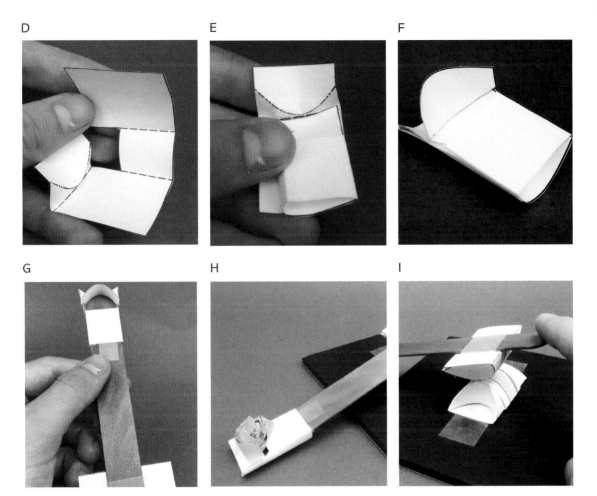

D E F

G H I

9. Roll the outside flap into the other flap and secure with tape (E, F).

10. Slide the cap onto the catapult arm and secure with tape (G).

11. Secure the base of the catapult to a solid surface (i.e., a table top or piece of heavy cardboard) using tape (H, I).

12. Ball up some of the paper scraps and place them in the seat created by the cap.

13. Press down on the catapult arm and launch your paper ball.

Unwrapping Sine Curves

Cylinders are one of three basic shapes, called developable shapes, that can be unwrapped. For example, a sphere cannot be unwrapped or rolled onto a flat plane. This can be seen in various maps of the world that have either distortion in the geography or many fingerlike projections that approximate a surface being unwrapped from the sphere.

In this activity, you will dip a cardboard cylinder (from a paper towel or toilet paper roll) into water at an angle, which is similar to cutting the cylinder with a plane at an angle. The resulting cross section will be an ellipse rather than a circle if you had cut the cylinder horizontally. After cutting the cardboard along the length of the tube, you can unfold it into a flat sheet, and the water line will create a sine curve. Another example of this would be cutting a cucumber at an angle. The slices would be oval or elliptical instead of circular. In this activity, as you unroll the cardboard cylinder into a flat surface, the ellipse will also unwrap onto a flat plane. The arc length of the ellipse will be preserved, but the shape will change into a sine curve. Developable shapes like the one in this activity are tied to curved-fold origami as the curved creases cause developable shapes to form. This activity demonstrates isometric principles of arc lengths being preserved when a surface is bent. Also, the math used in this activity helped to design the D-CORE joint, a joint that can collapse to a flat state and then deploy to its usable form.

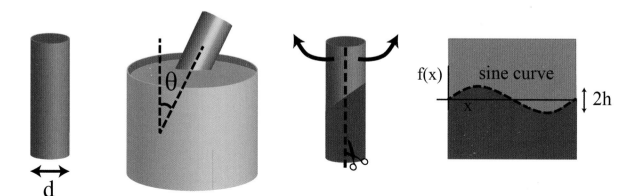

Now it's your turn:

For this activity you will need:
cardboard tube (like the ones on paper towels or toilet paper rolls)
bucket of water (or a plugged sink)
ruler
scissors
protractor (optional)
piece of string or floss long enough to wrap around the cardboard tube (optional)
calculator (optional)

1. Measure the diameter of your cardboard tube. Two ways of doing this include:
a. Using a ruler and measuring across the tube's cross section at its widest point.
b. Wrap string or floss around tube. Unwrap the string and measure its length. Divide this length by π (about 3.14) and you have your tube's diameter. Once you have a diameter from either of these methods, write it down (you will need it later).

$$d=\_\_\_\_\_$$

2. Take the cardboard tube and dip it into a bucket of water at an angle. Note this angle using a protractor or with some measurements and trigonometry. You may not be able to get an exact measurement, so an approximation will work. Write down this angle and call it θ.

$$\theta=\_\_\_\_\_$$

3. Carefully pull the cardboard tube out of the water and cut it along the length of the tube so you can unfold it to a flat sheet. The water line will unwrap into a sine curve. The height of the sine curve, let's call it h, can be calculated using the following formula where d is the diameter you measured in Step 1 and θ is the angle you found in Step 2:

$$h=d/2\tan(\theta)$$

What's more, you can now write the equation of your sine curve as:

$$f(x)=h\sin(2x/d)$$

Put this equation into a graphing calculator and see how it compares with the curve you made.

In addition to this activity, see what happens to your sine curve if you dip your tube in at different angles θ. This activity can also be done with a paint roller and a bucket of paint where you roll the paint onto a flat surface; of course, the results will be a bit more permanent. If dipping a cylinder in water and unrolling it gives a sine curve, what will happen if you dip a cone in water and unroll it the same way? Try it with a piece of paper.

ADVANCED
ACTIVITIES

FOLDING ALONG A CURVE

This activity teaches about the torsion of a curve along which paper is folded. A curve that is contained in a planar surface has zero torsion. A curve that is not contained in a planar surface has nonzero torsion. In this activity you will be able to observe that folding along arcs with distinct endpoints does not induce torsion in the curve. However, you will also observe that folding along simple closed curves generally does induce torsion in the curve.

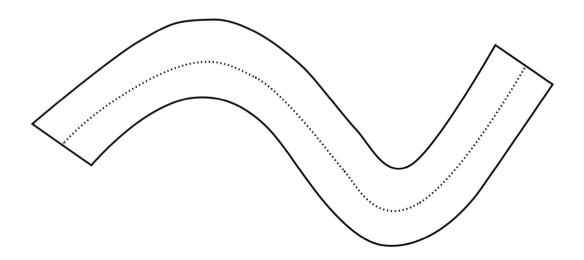

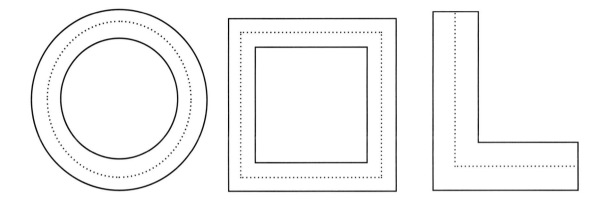

Now it's your turn:

1. Trace the dashed-line curve and the solid line neighborhood boundary of the curves indicated above with a pen or pencil. Press hard when tracing the dashed-line curve to create an indentation in your paper so that folding along the curve will be easier.

2. Cut out a neighborhood of the curve along the solid line. This will prevent self-intersections of the paper after it is folded.

3. Fold the paper along the curve.

4. If a crease does lie flat in a plane (on a table top), it is said to have zero torsion. Which type of curves produce creases that have zero torsion and which type of curves produce creases that have non-zero torsion? If you are unsure of your result, try narrowing the neighborhood.

In addition to using the graphics provided, you may also try drawing several curves of your own. Cut out a narrow neighborhood of each curve. Fold the paper along each curve. Observe the torsion of the folded curve in each case. Are your observations consistent with your conjecture in Step 4? If not, how can you rework your conjecture to be consistent with these new observations?

FLAT-FOLDING CONDITION

Origami art representing familiar objects or creatures is often constructed from flat-foldable bases devised to provide a sufficient number of flaps with sufficient amounts of paper to complete the design. Flat-foldability is also desirable to minimize the size of a structure in its folded state. This activity teaches more about flat-folding origami and uses the angles and crease assignments in any crease pattern to discover if the final design can fold flat or not. This activity verifies the Extended Kawasaki-Justin Theorem, which is one of the fundamental theorems of origami.

Kawasaki-Justin Theorem:
Let V be a vertex in an origami crease pattern and let $\theta_1, \theta_2, ..., \theta_n$ be the angles between consecutive creases going around the vertex (n must be even). Then the vertex can fold flat if and only if:

$$\theta_1 - \theta_2 + \theta_3 - \theta_4 + ... - \theta_n = 0.$$

Equivalently,

$$\theta_1 + \theta_3 + \theta_5 ... = \theta_2 + \theta_4 + \theta_6 ... = 180.$$

Extended Kawasaki-Justin Theorem:
Suppose there is a simple closed path on a crease pattern that intersects edges but not vertices. Pick a point P on the path; label the creases in the order that they are encountered as you travel around the path, and let $\theta_1, \theta_2, ..., \theta_n$ be the angles between consecutive creases encountered traveling along the path where θ_n is the angle between the last edge crossed and the first edge crossed. A necessary condition for the entire creae pattern to fold flat is that:

$$\theta_1 + \theta_3 + \theta_5 + ... + \theta_{(n-1)}$$

and

$$\theta_2 + \theta_4 + \theta_6 + ... + \theta_n$$

are multiples of 180 degrees.

An example of how this theorem is applied to a flat-foldable pattern is shown in Figure 1. (Notice the dip in the top left corner, θ_8 is negative because the curvature of the line goes clockwise rather than counterclockwise.)

Figure 1

Figure 2

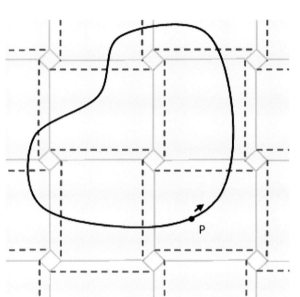

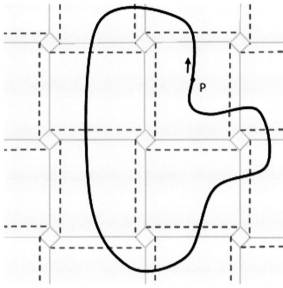

$\theta_1 = 0$	$\theta_2 = 0$
$\theta_3 = 0$	$\theta_4 = 90$
$\theta_5 = 0$	$\theta_6 = 90$
$\theta_7 = 0$	$\theta_8 = -90$
$\theta_9 = 0$	$\theta_{10} = 90$
$\theta_{11} = 0$	$\theta_{12} = 90$
$\theta_{13} = 0$	$\theta_{14} = 0$
$\theta_{15} = 0$	$\theta_{16} = 90$

Now it's your turn:
Verify the theorem for the indicated curve in Figure 2.
As you learned in Figure 1, the right side has two angles that will be negative because of the curve direction.
In addition, you may also sketch your own curve. Make sure your curve does not pass through any of the vertices. Choose a point on your curve and verify the theorem.
Just like in Figure 1, the right side has two angles that will be negative because of the curve direction.

LAYERING OF FOLDS

This activity provides more experience with flat-folding origami, and it uses flaps to help you visualize how the layers align in order to fold flat. The Three-Facet Theorem used here is one of the fundamental theorems of origami. This activity makes it possible to describe possible fold layerings and corresponding parity assignments.

Three-Facet Theorem:
Given three adjacent facets A, B, and C, wherein the folded form facet A overlaps crease BC and flap C overlaps crease AB as in Figure 1, facets A and C must lie on opposite sides of facet B.

Three-Facet Crease Assignment:
Given three adjacent facets A, B, and C, where in the folded form facet A overlaps crease BC and flap C overlaps crease AB as in Figure 1, creases AB and BC must have opposite parity.

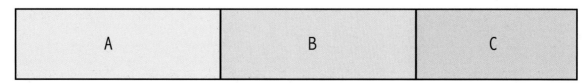

Figure 2

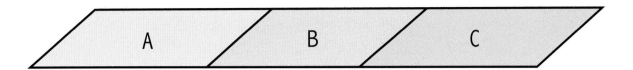

Now it's your turn:

1. Consider the diagram in Figure 1. If A and C are wider than B, then the only possible layering is A-B-C or C-B-A, where creases AB and BC have opposite parity (mountain and valley assignments).

2. What are possible layerings if A is wider than B and B is wider than C? What are the corresponding crease assignments? Demonstrate your answer by tracing, cutting out, and folding the pattern in Figure 2.

3. Given three adjacent facets A, B, and C, wherein the folded form facet A overlaps crease BC and flap C overlaps crease AB, what must be true about the positioning of facets A and C with respect to facet B in the folded form? (Hint: The facets should not be allowed to pass through one another.)

4. Given three adjacent facets A, B, and C, wherein the folded form facet A overlaps crease BC and flap C overlaps crease AB, what must be true about the parities of creases AB and BC? (Hint: Again, the facets should not be allowed to pass through one another.)

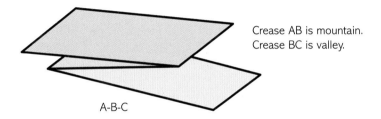

Crease AB is mountain.
Crease BC is valley.

A-B-C

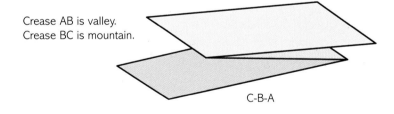

Crease AB is valley.
Crease BC is mountain.

C-B-A

Figure 1

THE BIG-LITTLE-BIG ANGLE THEOREM

This activity teaches the concepts of the Big-Little-Big Angle Theorem and the Unique Largest Angle Theorem in the case of a single degree-4 vertex flat-foldable pattern.

The Big-Little-Big Angle Theorem:
In a flat-foldable pattern, at any vertex, the creases on either side of any sector whose angle is smaller than those of its neighbors must have an anto (opposite) crease assignment.
The following result is a corollary.

Unique Largest Angle Theorem:
In a flat-foldable pattern at a degree-4 vertex, if there is a unique largest sector angle, its crease assignment must be an iso (the same) crease assignment.

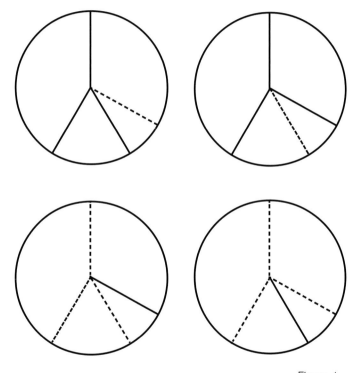

Figure 1

Now it's your turn:

This activity deals with flat-foldable patterns with a single degree-4 vertex.

Case 1: There is a unique smallest sector in the pattern.

In Figure 1, the four possible crease assignments for this case are shown. Note that the smallest sector always has an anto (opposite) crease assignment from its neighbors and the largest sector always has an iso (the same) crease assignment.

Trace and then cut out these patterns and verify that they are flat-foldable with the given crease assignments.

Case 2: There are two consecutive smallest sectors in the pattern.

In Figure 2, a possible crease assignment for this case is given. What are the other five possible crease assignments?

Case 3: There are three consecutive smallest sectors in the pattern.

Note that in this case, all sectors must have angles measuring 90 degrees (see the Maekawa-Justin Theorem). What are the eight possible crease assignments? How many patterns are unique, allowing rotation?

For additional practice:

By folding a piece of paper, construct your own single degree-4 vertex flat-foldable pattern. This can be done by folding two adjacent creases and then folding the paper across both creases at the same time, pressing the paper down flat to create two additional creases. Label each crease and note its crease assignments (mountain or valley). Verify that the smallest sector has anto and the largest sector has iso crease assignments.

What are the other possible crease assignments that will produce a flat-folding with the same creases? Verify your claim in each case by refolding the paper with the new crease assignment.

Now try giving the smallest sector an iso crease assignment. Demonstrate that the pattern is not flat foldable.

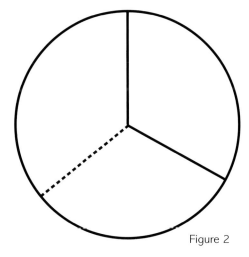

Figure 2

FLAT-FOLDABLE VERTEX DEGREE

This activity teaches the concept of the Maekawa-Justin Theorem, which is one of the fundamental theorems of origami. You will use the crease types in this activity to determine whether or not a fold pattern can fold flat. You will also identify the relationship between the number of mountain and valley creases to form a flat-foldable vertex.

Maekawa-Justin Theorem:
For any flat-foldable vertex, let M be the number of mountain folds at the vertex, and let V be the number of valley folds. Then:

$$M-V=\pm 2$$

Corollary: For any flat-foldable vertex, the degree at the vertex is even.

Now it's your turn:
The following are proposed patterns for a single vertex flat folding. Count the number of mountain and valley creases in each case. Now copy the crease pattern on separate sheets of paper and try to fold them. What do you notice?

Is it possible to create a single vertex flat folding with an odd number of creases? Give it a try.

If a single flat-folding vertex has three mountain creases, what are the possible numbers of valley creases?

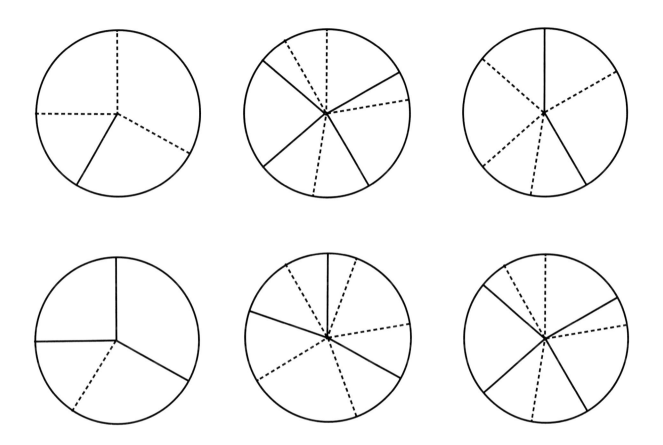

HULL'S CONSECUTIVE SECTORS

This activity teaches the concept of the Hull's Consecutive Sectors Theorem and will make it possible for you to identify the possible crease assignments for consecutive identical sectors in a single vertex flat-foldable pattern.

Hull's Consecutive Sectors: Let $(\theta_1, \theta_2, ..., \theta_k)$ be a sequence of consecutive identical sector angles in a flat-foldable vertex of degree $N>k$. Then a crease assignment for the $k+1$ distinct creases surrounding these sectors is valid only if:

$M-V=\pm 1$ when k is even
$M-V=0$ when k is odd,

where M is the number of mountain folds and V is the number of valley folds.
If $N = k$, then a crease assignment of the k distinct creases of the vertex is valid only if $M-V=\pm 2$.

Now it's your turn:
Besides paper and pencil, you will need a protractor.
The following are patterns for a single vertex flat folding with k consecutive identical sectors. Count the number of mountain and valley assignments for the $k+1$ distinct creases surrounding these sectors. What pattern do you notice? Does it make a difference if k is even or odd?
Now design an example where all N sectors are identical. In this case, each angle will be 360/N degrees. What is now true about the number of mountain and valley assignments? Can you reconcile your new observations with your observation above?

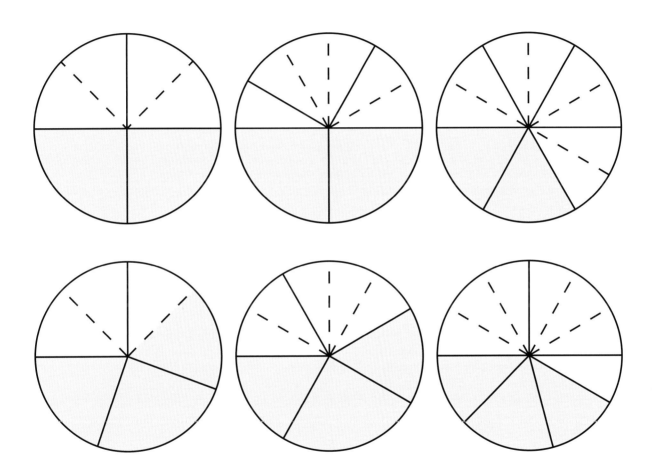

HALF-PLANE THEOREMS

This activity teaches the concepts of the Degree-4 Vertices Half-Planes and Vertex Folded Form Half-Planes Theorems. The activity will make it possible for you to recognize that in the crease pattern of a flat-foldable degree-4 vertex, every half-plane contains at least one crease of the majority type. Also, you will be able to recognize that in the folded flat-foldable vertex, every crease lies within a common half-plane.

Degree-4 Vertices

Half-Planes Theorem: In the crease pattern of a flat-foldable degree-4 vertex, every half-plane contains at least one crease of the majority type.

Vertex-Folded Form

Half-Planes Theorem: In the folded form of a flat-foldable vertex, every crease lies within a common half-plane.

Now it's your turn:

A. Folding Pattern and Half-Planes
Consider the single vertex degree-4 flat-folding pattern shown in Figure 1. There are three mountain folds and one valley fold that meet at a common vertex V. Mark the midpoint of the edge of a piece of paper and label it X. Place the paper over half of the pattern so that X is positioned at V. Rotate the paper keeping the point X at V. Is there any point in the rotation at which all mountain folds are covered?   What is the maximum number

Figure 1

Figure 2

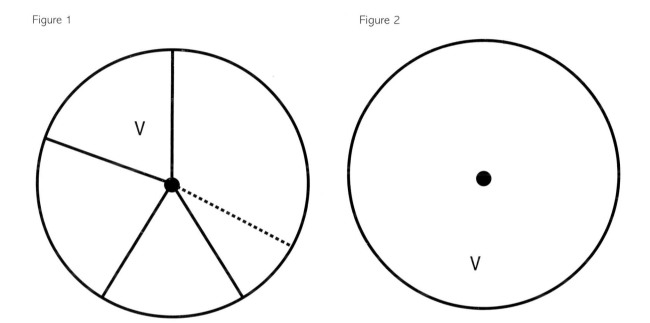

of mountain folds that can be covered? Now sketch your own single vertex degree-4 pattern with three mountain folds and one valley fold so that all three mountain folds can be covered with your paper positioned such that X is placed at the vertex V. Can this be a flat-folding pattern? (Hint: Consider the Kawasaki-Justin Theorem from previous activity.)

B. Folded Form and Half-Planes
What happens when the pattern in Figure 1 is folded? Is there a way to position your paper used in part A such that X is placed at the vertex V and the entire folded form is covered?

Can you create a different pattern in Figure 2 so that you get a different result? Give it a try.
In addition: Explain why a folded form of a single vertex degree-4 flat-folding pattern can always be covered by a half-plane bounded by a line through the vertex.

NEW
ORIGAMI

RIGIDLY FOLDABLE TESSELLATIONS

A tessellation is a tiling pattern that uses one or more geometric shapes, called tiles, to fill a flat surface with no overlapping or gaps between tiles. In an origami tessellation, the fold lines of the crease pattern divide up the flat sheet into a pattern of geometric tiles. However, where most tessellations exist only on 2-D planes, folding along the lines of an origami tessellation creates complex and interesting 3-D surfaces. Recent work by BYU and Robert Lang has established mathematics that can be used to create new origami tessellations. Several new rigidly foldable tessellation crease patterns are presented on the following pages.

Alternating Level Shifter:
This tessellation uses chains of level shifters to achieve motion.
As can be seen in the fold pattern, these chains alternate in fold parity.

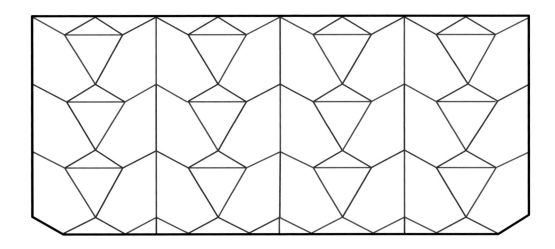

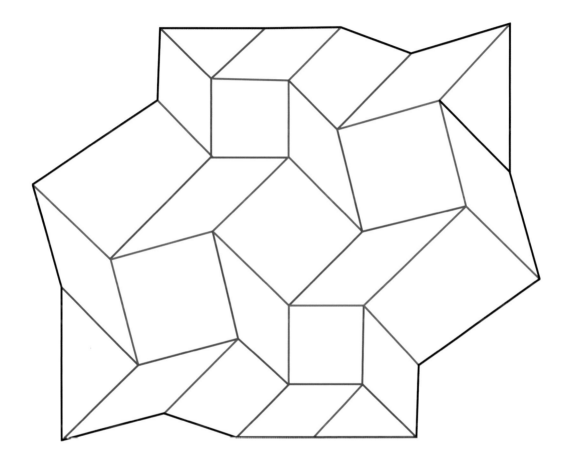

Dual Square Twist:
This tessellation uses two square twists with different twist angles.
These two twists use squares of different sizes as can be seen in the fold pattern.

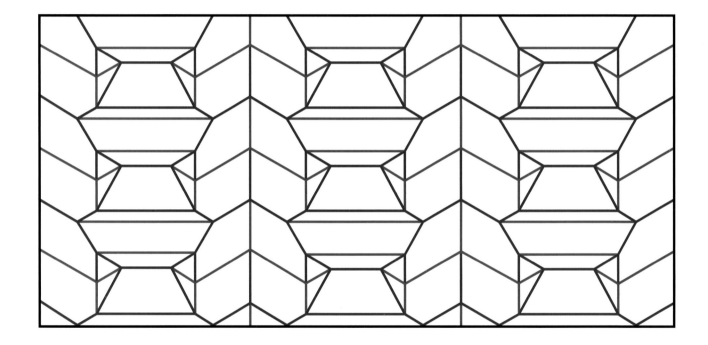

Triple Parallel:
This tessellation is a modification of the Miura-Ori, which replaces every other chain of vertices with a new fold pattern while preserving the original motion of the Miura-Ori.

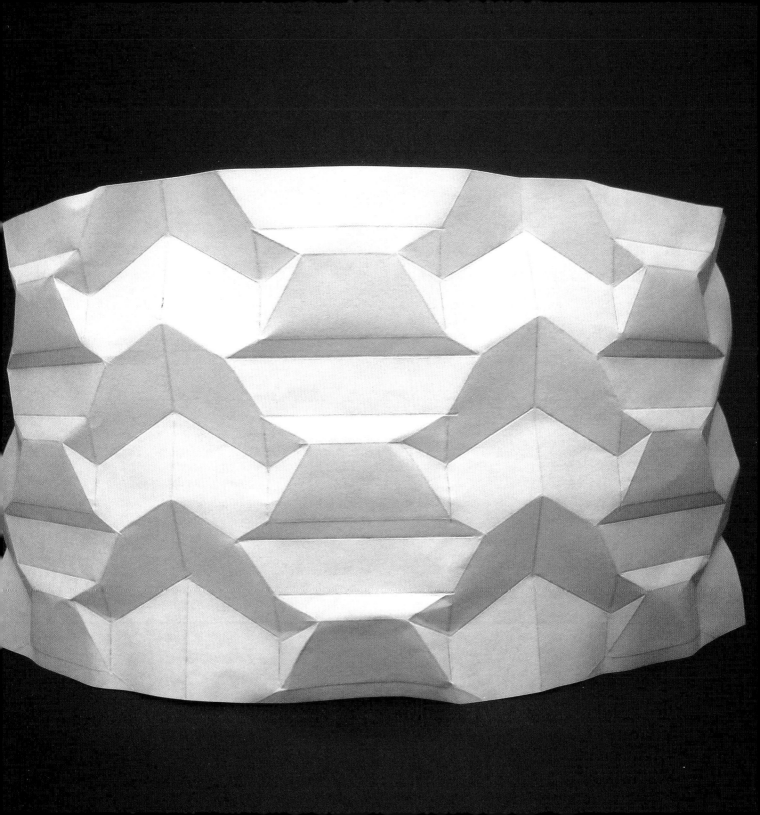

MOTHER AND CHILD

ORIGAMI ART BY MATTHEW GONG

The piece "Mother and Child" was designed by origami artist and student Matthew Gong. The juxtaposition between mother and child shows the importance of a mother teaching a child. The mother has already fully developed into maturity. Her moments of joy and pain are like folds, each crease strengthening her character. They give her strength and beauty. The child is still innocent and pure. With fewer folds, he is curious and has much more to learn in life. These figures express the relationship between mother and child.

If you look closely you can see similarities between the folding structure of the mother and child. The mother has some additional features but the underlying structure is quite similar.

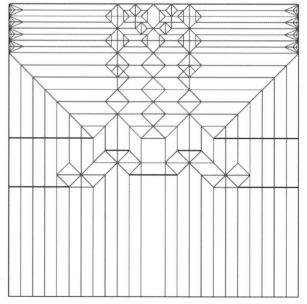

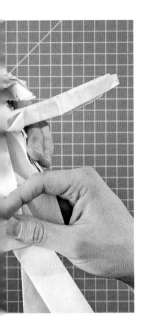

The "Mother" in the process
of being folded.

EXHIBITIONS

Dutch Design Week 2013, Eindhoven, The Netherlands
Clerkenwell Design Week 2014, London, England
Designarts Utah 2014, Utah, USA
BYU Museum of Art 2015, Utah, USA
Dutch Design Week 2015, Eindhoven, The Netherlands
Design March 2015, Reykjavik, Iceland
Chimei Museum 2016, Tainan, Taiwan
Interior Design Show 2017, Toronto, Canada

CITATIONS

[1] Lang, R. J., 1997. *Origami in Action.* St. Martin's Griffin.
[2] Shafer, J., 2001. *Origami to Astonish and Amuse.* St. Martin's Griffin.
[3] Shafer, J., 2010. *Origami Ooh La La! Action Origami for Performance and Play.* Createspace Independent Publishing Platform.
[4] Hoberman, C., 1991. Reversibly Expandable Structures. United States Patent No. 4,981,732.
[5] http://www.fluxfurniture.com
[6] Lang, R. J., 2013. One Ellipse to Rule Them All. The Fold (Origami USA).
[7] Demaine, E., O'Roarke, J., 2007. *Geometric Folding Algorithms.* Cambridge University Press.
[8] Houdini, H., 2001. *Houdini's Paper Magic.* Fredonia Books.
[9] Wilcox, H. W. K., 1873. National Standards and Emblems. *Harper's Magazine.* http://www.harpers.org/archive/1873/07/0057479

ACKNOWLEDGEMENTS

Many, many people have been involved in the work described in this book, and still others have been involved in the creation of the book itself. We would like to particularly thank Patsy Wang-Iverson for her encouragement on the project. A big thanks to all who have contributed! An incomplete list of contributers is provided below.

Authors
David C. Morgan
Denise M. Halversen
Spencer P. Magleby
Terri C. Bateman
Larry L. Howell

Assistant Editors
Jared Butler
Kaleb Garlick
Brandon Hanna
Blake Hoover
Tamara Pace Thomson

Book Designer
Camrie Smith

Graphic Designers
Yeeun Koo
Judith Westwood
Joshua Siebert
David C. Morgan

Content Contributors
Quentin Allen
Quentin Aten
Alex Avila
Bryce Barker
Landen Bowen
Jared Bruton
Sandra Burnett
Dakota Burrow
Jared Butler
BYU Photography
Eric Call
Erica Crampton
Nichole Cross
Jason Dearden
Isaac Delimont
Luke Dickenson
Joey Eddington
Bryce Edmondson
Thomas Evans
Janette Fernelius
Kevin Francis
Madison Fujimoto
Matthew Gong

Clayton Grames
Holly Greenberg
Jacob Greenwood
Haden Heath
Blake Hoover
Jordan Parcell Hosler
Brian Jensen
Diane Kay
Robert Lang
Josh Lindmark
Dalip Malla
Michael McCain
Brett Mellor
Ezekiel Merriam
Jessica Morgan
Michael Morgan
Sean Moore
Nathan Mooth
Andrew Moulton
Kyle Murray
Todd Nelson
Cory Newton
Jeffrey Niven

Jemi Ong
Millie Parkinson
Nathan Pehrson
John Pierce
Steve Puertas
Aaron Puglisi
David Richardson
Jacob Robinson
Levi Rupert
Peter Schleede
Daniel Shirley
Kenny Seymour
Joshua Siebert
Kyler Tolman
Brian Trease
Samantha Van Slooten
Patrick Walton
Eric Wilcox
Sam Wilding
Mary Wilson
Trent Zimmerman
Shannon Zirbel

FUNDING SOURCES

This material is based on work supported by the National Science Foundation and the Air Force Office of Scientific Research under NSF Grant EFRI-ODISSEI-1240417.

Partners

NASA
GE Healthcare
Jet Propulsion Laboratory
Wasatch Design Collective
Robert J. Lang Origami
Intuitive Surgical
Tessel
QuickStove
BYU CMR
Crocker Ventures

Other partners have provided important support through financial and/or technical contributions.